BEHIND GYM DOORS

**THE WEIRD AND WONDERFUL WORLD OF FITNESS AS TOLD
BY ONE OF LONDON'S MOST EXCLUSIVE TRAINERS**

MATT HODGES

BEHIND
GYM
DOORS

THE WEIRD AND WONDERFUL WORLD OF FITNESS AS TOLD
BY ONE OF LONDON'S MOST EXCLUSIVE TRAINERS

MATT HODGES

FITNESS

/ FIT-NIS/

— noun

1.   The state of being physically healthy and strong.

2.   The body's capability of distributing inhaled oxygen, to muscle tissue during increased physical effort.

3.   Ignore points 1 and 2. A now bastardised idea that seeks to play on your insecurities, and encourage you to part with your money. Otherwise known as 'Fitniz'.

4.   See Fitness Industry, Social Media Influencers and Celebrity Weight Loss fads.

CONTENTS

PROLOGUE
LEGGY LEGRA

It was 2015, just a few months after I launched my first studio in Hampstead, North London, the city's wealthiest community, when an horrific trip to hospital took place.

Most of my clients booked me via my website, and this young Russian woman was one of my first major (rich) clients. She had sent me an enquiry and told me she was looking to get in shape before her son's parents' evening at school.

That's got to be a joke, right? I thought to myself, reading the enquiry. Well, no; keeping up an elite appearance is not uncommon in Hampstead, so I thought little of it at the time.

It wasn't long before the Russian woman – let's call her 'AllEGra' – was walking through the studio entrance. Allegra instantly knocked me for six at how beautiful she was. Six-foot-tall, legs up to my chin and a face not too dissimilar to those that grace the catwalks of London Fashion Week. Androgynous, but beautifully so.

However, it wouldn't be long before I'd realise that she had the body of a Greek goddess but with the brain of a Greek salad.

She was already in what we fitness professionals call 'shape', so I was interested to see how much further she wanted to push herself.

Within a few minutes of our first session, what struck me the most was that every time Allegra moved her legs, she sounded like a TV suffering from interference.

Crackle - crackle.

Every step.

Crackle - crackle.

Could it be that her pair of custom Nike Air's bubble had a puncture? Was she in fact a humanoid and these were her badly-oiled joints creaking? Or did she have a Quality Street fetish and was stashing empty wrappers in her drawers? As a fitness professional, I did my best to ignore the noise and concentrated on trying not to show my confusion as I evaluated her health and body movement.

Thirty minutes in, however, the noise remained loud and crackly.

Then, I noticed she was overheating and her ankles had turned blue while she was on the spin bike. Curiosity got the better of me and I broke the patter with genuine concern.

'Erm, are you OK, Allegra?' I ask. 'Your ankles don't look … kosher.'

What an understatement. Her ankles looked like they would give Violet Beauregarde a run for her money.

'I zaw zis in Cozmo, it good for fat loss,' she replies in a thick Russian accent pointing towards her feet.

(Be thankful this isn't the audiobook. Whenever I try to do a Russian accent, it always sounds more Basil Fawlty Hitleresque than actual Russian.)

'Erm, what's good for fat loss?' I reply, knowing I'm not going to like what I hear.

'Zis zellophane,' she says. 'You wrap yourself and you lose ze fat.'

I take a good ten seconds to decipher the word 'zellophane'. Aeroplane? Cello pain?

'Sorry. Come again.' The penny drops and I gawp. 'You're

using cellophane to lose weight?'

'Yez, it very good!'

By now, not only had Allegra's ankles turned bright blue, but she was overheating faster than a politician on Question Time.

'Let's get you off the bike, girl; something's not right,' I say, now realising that this dim bulb had mummified her legs in sandwich wrapping, cutting off valuable circulation.

And then, with an impressive swan dive that would challenge Tom Daly for his medals, Allegra dismounted the bike in one casual collapse.

So, here I am, in my studio with a Russian supermodel who's passed out on the floor because she thought it was a good idea to wrap her legs in cling film in order to lose weight. Oh, thank you very much glossy magazines. Thank you very much.

'999. What's your emergency, please?' the soft voice on the other end of my iPhone 7 was reassuring.

'Ambulance, please,' I reply, taking my client's pulse, and checking her airway was clear of loose clothing, OTT jewellery and cling film.

Ten minutes later, the ambulance had rushed Allegra and me to the local A&E. Following a quick bout of resuscitation, and unwrapping from all the cling film, my client's temperature is normal again. I pretend I'm concerned but all I am worried about is the imminent arrival of her next of kin. Allegra had spoken of him briefly at the beginning of our session and I sensed he was not one for romantic comedies. Cue the silver Mercedes G Series with blacked-out windows screeching up at the front of A&E.

I'm a dead man. I'm sure of it.

I wait patiently outside the hospital and listen to my heartbeat thump loudly in my ears. Judgement Day is here. Sauron is about to lay the smackdown on Middle Earth, and there's no James Bond coming to save me in the nick of time. I'm expecting a 10-foot, leather-clad, knife-wielding, bouncer-type manscaped within an inch of his own life with huge war scars striped across his face to beat me to within an inch of my own life with my own shoes.

Instead, to my surprise, a small Russian doll of a dude steps out of the vehicle, spots me and calmly walks over. 'Are you… Matt? You did vell, zankyou.' He puts his little Oddjob hand inside his well-laundered suit jacket.

I fully expected him to pull a shiv and stab me in my stomach Gulag style and I brace for impact. Instead, he pulls out a massive wodge of crisp notes and siphons off more £50 notes than I could count. Easily more than two grand. He hands the notes to me with a crooked smile.

No gold teeth.

'For your… troublez,' he says.

I stand there gobsmacked. But, thankfully, not literally. I look at him dumbfounded. He looks back at me with a careful confidence of a man who knows that he has just bought my silence. He grabs my hand and firmly places his other hand on top of it.

'Zank you.' He nods, looks at me dead in the eye, and then walks into the hospital.

I take a seat on a squeaky plastic chair and place my now drenched hands onto my head and breathe a sigh of relief.

To say the situation is surreal is an understatement. Not only had I had just lived through my own personal Bond movie, I had a fistful of money in my pocket.

Suffice it to say I never saw Allegra again. I like to think she was sent back to the warehouse where she was made for re-wiring, or progressed to more heavy-duty way of losing fat, like self-amputation.

I'd like to say that her kind – rich, stupid and careless girlfriends who feel forced to stay thin and taut – are rare in the fitness industry, but, as you'll soon discover, this was just another 'normal' day in the life of an in-demand personal trainer to the world's elite.

INTRODUCTION

Do you know who I am?

Probably not but don't worry, I'm not offended. I'm a small fish in a big sea, an ocean overrun by wannabe and has-been 'fitness influencers'.

I don't have a large social media following; I am not a regular on daytime TV; I don't tell you how to live your life in lifestyle magazines. Whatever they are. But I do have a story to tell.

I've spent the last sixteen years working as a personal trainer and massage therapist, building up my own company and brand. In that time, I have witnessed some of the most famous faces in the world in their most compromised, intimate moments. It is those events that provide the backdrop for this book, stories which have never been told to anyone before now (well, not publicly), and which will shock even the most liberal of readers. My aim with this book is to entertain, firstly, and leave you yearning for more. But also to inform, illuminate, educate – because I don't think even the most fitness-savvy person has any clue on what actually happens behind the scenes in the fitness industry.

I went from working a regular nine-to-five, hidden behind a computer screen as a graphic designer, drinking too much free coffee, and hating mundane small talk at the obligatory after-work drinks, to becoming one of a select few PTs employed by the world's rich, famous and elite.

Billionaires.

Popstars.

Politicians.

A-Z celebrities.

World-class athletes.

Rich-as-fuck nobodies.

I've seen them all.

You could say I was one of the few personal trainers in London who made it 'big' but you'd be wrong. The clients I had were *so* exclusive, that I was contractually gagged from publicly discussing or promoting my work, bogged down daily by reams of Non-Disclosure Agreements, meaning no one ever knew how successful my business had truly become. I was not allowed to post before/after pictures or hashtag my clients' progress in #TransformationTuesday. I was invisible in a world of ultra-high visibility. Believe me when I say life on a gym floor is not all it's cracked up to be.

During my career, I have lost everything, gained it all back, and battled my own wavering mental health – pretty severe demons – along the way. I have questioned every ounce of my physical and mental state, and I have been on the verge of quitting multiple times. But me being the stubborn bugger I am, I bled, sweated and teared my way through it all, kept anything-but-calm and carried on. Somehow, I always found the magic in helping others achieve what they thought was impossible. For every 'askhole' or 'money is no object' client I have met (and there have been a lot), there was always one diamond in the rough that cemented my reason to continue.

So, this life story is a collection of tall-but-true tales brought to life by the many complex characters that I have encountered in nearly twenty years. It is an honest and raw account of the personalities and the quite frankly ridiculous moments I have witnessed up close and very personal indeed.

Many of the stories will make you laugh, some will leave you feeling uncomfortable, some might even make you want to hurl up last night's quinoa and boiled chicken, and some will leave you feeling an immense sense of sadness. But, trust me, it's the clients who look like they are living the dream who are the most insecure and lonely. Their beautiful lives, constantly on show on the 'Gram', is a world away from the barbells and burpees that I have been privy to in real life.

So, in 2022, as I embark on the next chapter of my own life (God knows where … thanks Covid), I feel now is the perfect opportunity to tell you the truth, the whole truth … and nothing but the truth.

You'll have questions along the way, for sure. Like, 'What the hell is it really like training the celebrity circuit?' and 'What's it like mingling with billionaires, the super elite and the world's most wanted?' and, hopefully, 'Why are so many companies profiting off useless products and bad nutrition claims, and how the hell can Z-List reality stars become trainers and nutritionists overnight?'

I have the answers, I think. And, as you've picked this book up, chances are you'll be wanting the answers too.

The Fitness Industry is fuelled by so much batshit bullshit, so I'm here to be your personal guide to cut through it all. With a little help from the clients and characters I have met along the way, I am here to tell it as it is. And how it could be.

This book is not all about weights and crunches, and I've spared you the pretentious quotes such as 'Live, Love and Lift Weights'. I'm not going to preach at you or tell you that you need to detox your liver or rebalance your gut biomes. And there are definitely no glossy 15-minute cooking recipes or home workout programs, or telling you that if you hang from your ceiling you will get 'ripped' in 15 seconds.

Because that's all lies.

No, this is an unadulterated account of the characters and stories that I've been fortunate (and, in some cases, unfortunate) enough to experience. You'll learn about the misfits, the degenerates, the chancers, the takers, the morally corrupt and the bullshit artists, all aiming for outer perfection without looking within first. Together, we'll explore the lives of the rich and famous, the truth behind those Hollywood bodies, and the realities of the health and fitness trends that clog up your social media accounts on a daily basis – all through my life. Because I've lived it.

You'll learn why you should never keep your mouth open during a massage, why you should always keep your mouth shut when talking to the Russian mafia, and why drinking your own urine is never a good idea …

Hang on tight, because as wild and surreal as this book sometimes gets, the incidents, stories, and people … are *all* real … and they really did happen.

Let's go…

DISCLAIMER

Before we continue together, I must tell you that my finger-wagging lawyer has strongly advised me that I must respect the rules of client confidentiality, even though some of my ex-clients don't deserve it.

Therefore, regardless of whether they were a client, an employer, a friend or a fellow personal trainer – I've changed their names. I have also amalgamated or tweaked characters, stories, locations and timelines. This is purely to protect us all, and to avoid being contacted by a 'No Win, No Fee' solicitor.

All you really need to know though is that this stuff really fucking happened.

THE THREE AMIGOS

There are people in your life who you will always remember. There are the people who stay, and the people who go. There are those who linger like a bad smell, and those who are unforgettable. There are those who you like and love, and those who you dislike and can't get rid of. And then there are those who break your balls so hard you just can't help but love them anyway. This story is about those people – my friends – and they crop up more than once in this book.

I do not suffer fools. I enjoy my own company, and I choose my friends wisely. There are over seven billion people on this planet but there are only two I like.

Ladies and gentlemen, may I present to you all 'Mikey the Danger Toddler', and 'Man Like Irish', otherwise known as Irish. Together, we are the Three Amigos.

Before we get into the nitty-gritty of the stories, I want to introduce you to these two degenerate imbeciles – who could have a separate book written about them. But given that they were present for most of the stories in this book then it would be an injustice not to formally tell you about them.

First up, may I introduce to you the legend, the one and only, the man who gave Mona Lisa her smile, the fella who, when doing push-ups, doesn't push himself up, but instead pushes the earth down. The man who sleeps with a nightlight, not because he's scared of the dark, but because the dark is scared of him. A drum roll, please ...

Mikey, 'The Danger Toddler' or as I like to call him – 'Danger'.

A smidgen taller than five-and-a-half feet, Danger got a two-part nickname because, one, he's a carefree cheeky bastard who isn't afraid of a confrontation and, two, he is the Peter Pan of the fitness industry. He's now in his early forties but he genuinely still looks about 23.

A sharp-talking barrow boy personal trainer with the libido of a Viagra-filled jackrabbit, Danger is the Jekyll to my Mr. Hyde. The Quagmire to my Peter Griffin. Wherever I am, Danger is not too far away, either taking the piss out of me or trying to sleep with my, his – anyone's – clients. Being a female left in a room alone with Danger will either get you laid or get you filing a lawsuit. That said, if you ever need backing up, or a friend to lend an ear, Danger suddenly becomes as loyal as a homeless person is to a can of Super Tennents.

There really is too much to say about Danger here, but you should know that he is my ride or die and has stuck beside me through thick and thin. Our banter backgammon started when he nicknamed me 'Boodles', after I rinsed him for eating butternut squash noodles and the name has stuck ever since.

We both started working together in a membership, or High Street, gym in and around 2009 and then moved on to a celebrity one-to-one joint, which I'll talk about in the next chapter. We were wet behind the ear PTs, looking to earn a quick buck and cut our teeth on unsuspecting treadmill victims. Or, in Danger's case, a chance to get on the top totty list with the UK's rich and famous. He believes they have 'better sex and cocaine' and he may well be right.

While I was very 'by the book', Danger, on the other hand, was the complete opposite. For the life of me I don't know why we clicked, because, really, we were chalk and cheese. Whilst I was writing training programs in my lunch break, Danger was chatting up the receptionist, or pouring himself free cups of coffee from the new Nespresso machine that the gym had bought for the staff, just to take the edge off the ridiculous quotas we had to fill each month.

He, not unlike the coffee machine, didn't last long.

Hot on his tail, it wasn't too long before I'd got sick of the long hours and the low wages, and decided it was time to change, so our paths took a different turn. Danger decided he liked the regularity of new females in chain gyms and has worked in and out of these for as long as I've known him. I'm sure other PTs in London will appreciate that the city is actually quite small, and the PT industry is even smaller. Eventually, all PTs end up knowing or working with every other PT throughout our careers, so it wasn't long before Danger and I were reunited at a one-to-one studio in Central London.

It was here that we'd meet our trifecta of awesomeness, the third wheel, the last musketeer who comes in the form of a squat, muscular, bald-headed, ginger-bearded PT we both liked to call 'Man Like Irish'.

Whilst Irish and I are still friends to this day, our career paths didn't intertwine as much as mine and Danger's. So, I'll tell you a little more about the man himself in this chapter and you'll hear more about the boob hungry he-pony that Mikey is later.

Irish was born and bred in Ballymun, Dublin. For those who don't know, Ballymun was built to alleviate the housing crisis in the 1960s after people were being killed by poor workmanship on local houses. High-rises and tower blocks were built that harboured a huge heroin crisis and bred a distinct hardness to the locals. Irish was one of them. Hardman, not heroin addict.

I first met Irish when he joined the chain gym that Danger and I were working at. I remember the day he started, when he approached the two female receptionists at the front desk wielding a Gaelic hurling stick.

'What's the story, horse?' he said to one of the girls.

He used to call everyone horse for a reason he never made clear.

'Oi'm here ta speak to the manager,' he continued in his

thick Irish accent. 'Tell him Oi'm here fer the personal training job so Oi am.'

Both receptionists bolted for the staff room door thinking he was some form of terrorist.

Danger, seeing no cause for alarm, promptly approached him, shook his hand and asked the guy why he was carrying a 'long fucking stick'.

'What in the Jaysus. This is a hurlin' stick ya wee idjit, away and wash the back o' ye bollocks,' he said, looking at Mikey like he'd just insulted his mother.

Danger looked at me, I waited for it to kick off, but instead he just shrugged, turned his back on Irish and then waddled off reciting: 'Away and wash the back o ye bollox,' in his Cockney accent, forgetting that just behind him is an irate Irishman with half an oak tree in his hand.

It transpired that Irish was indeed there for the PT job, he just had to leave his bat behind. And, to his credit, he was actually a good trainer.

After their initial meeting, Danger and Irish evened out their differences in the following weeks. Irish thought Danger was a 'wee gobshite', whilst Danger thought nothing more of insulting the Irish (even though his mum is Irish) and quoting reasons why gingers weren't half as strong as brunettes especially ones who grew up in high-rises and played 'hockey with helmets'.

The irony is that Irish was next-level strong for someone who spent as much time horizontal as he did talking about the times when, back in Ballymun, he and the other scrotey little guttersnipes would make videos where they'd terrorise the Garda on their stolen motorbikes. In all the time I knew Irish, I saw him train only a handful of times and he was renowned for eating anything he could get his hands on. He was a bit of an anomaly like that – greedy he was, fat he wasn't. The only thing I can attribute his low body fat percentage to was another irony all on its own, because the intention didn't meet the reality.

A few years ago when NEAT (Non-Exercise Activity Thermogenesis or in layman's terms – the amount of energy [calories] you expend when doing anything that is non exercise related, eating or sleeping, for example) – became 'fashionable' every PT from here to Antarctica started talking about how many steps you needed to take a day, which went against everything Irish was aiming for in his own personal life (the little and the least amount of effort possible to get the job done).

To quote Irish on NEAT:

'Oi'm fuckin bored a-this shite, why can't ya just leave a man in peace and let him rest will ye.' (Or…'I am completely over this rigmarole, why can't normal folk just leave a good fellow to get on with his rest days.')

To counteract this wave of thinking, Irish came up with a hare-brained idea to name his dog Miles (later to be made famous on social media memes).

How you may ask?

Well, when someone asked how many steps he'd taken, he could just say that he walked Miles every day (not entirely original you might say but Irish didn't seem to care). And yet the second irony here is that he did actually walk miles, with Miles, every day thus keeping his body fat down. To say that the Irish fulfil their stereotype of not being the brightest of buttons, in this instance, would be an oversight. I thought it a quite remarkably clever way of justifying the ability to do as little as possible. He got enough exercise pushing his luck, but it clearly did the job.

After a year of us all working together, we'd all become bosom buddies, and God protect anyone who came into contact with all three of us because they were just a lamb to the slaughter – one of which was Jonnie, to whom I dedicate a chapter later on. There have been so many other wild characters along the way, such as Kane, who if it wasn't for the fact that he hated all of us, could well have been our fourth Amigo. I have left some of them out for their own safety, or our safety – I can't decide which, but above all, I want to acknowledge that like any good friend, you don't have to see them every day to appreciate that they're still there. When we meet it's like we were never apart.

And that's the making of the Three Amigos.

PART ONE

A HELLO FROM CELEBRITYVILLE

LESSON ONE:

It's always underwhelming meeting your idol. It's even worse training your idol. Sometimes, realising that celebrities are just humans levels the playing field. That is, of course, unless they think they're in the corporate box looking down on you playing. Never let a client take the piss out of your mum, never give them a free ticket to anything, and definitely, definitely don't let them show you their latest STD.

My journey started similarly to many other trainers, in a *completely* different industry. In 2005, I graduated from the University of Loughborough with a degree in Industrial Design. I ended up selling my soul to the London rat-race, working the normal nine-to-five in the city as a graphic designer. I loosely say nine-to-five, because my boss didn't give two hoots about the amount of overtime I put in that went unnoticed and was never rewarded. (I can't complain, it served me well when I entered the fitness industry). But it didn't take long before I was bored off my tits working for The Man in an industry not too dissimilar to Brazilian Jiu Jitsu, which takes years to reap any rewards.

For those who don't know, Loughborough University is famed for its sports, so along with my design degree, I'd picked up the workout bug that many young adult men get into and, if I may say so myself, I got into pretty good shape. It was circa 2006-7 when I was flitting between training, design work and some freelance PT that I managed to obtain from working out in my local membership gym. I wasn't qualified then but, as I was to come to quickly learn, qualifications didn't matter anyway. Still don't, it seems, as you'll see later. Training was taking over, and I knew that it was time to change careers when I was repeatedly asked at job interviews, 'What do you think your strengths are?' and I would want to reply, 'Chest, Shoulders, Biceps and Traps'.

It was time to say 'sayonara, sucker' to the design industry.

After a period of time dabbling in a bit of what morons now call 'Fitness Modelling', I was scouted by an agent and strangely found myself on the set of *EastEnders* (one of the most popular soaps in the UK where every scene is a conflict).

My part was 'Neil', barman of the R&R club. Invited for an 'on-screen' audition, I had to parade around on set – with my clothes off. I soon found out that even before Instagram you could get telly work just by showing your abs! It was a good gig and it paid pretty well for the time. Plus, it got me out of the nine-to-five. I also got to eat whenever I wanted to, and train at sociable hours.

The story was written, (in my head, anyway) that I was now going to become an actor. I could see it: the bright lights of Hollywood, fans fainting as I walked into my local Tesco, teenage girls screaming to get my autograph every time I parked my banged-up Vauxhall Corsa in the 'extras' car park. Predictably, the dream was over as soon as it began.

However, what did happen, thanks to my abs on-screen time, was that I soon gained a healthy list of celebrity clients. Sorry, 'Celebrity' clients. Again, I still hadn't officially qualified as a PT, but I trained them anyway … until one of them ballsed-up a single leg squat and landed on their face. Then it dawned on me: I was unqualified, unprotected, and had no 'real' world experience. I needed insurance.

Time to get qualified.

The Level Three PT course took me a total of three months to complete, including another month to train as a massage therapist (the idea of massaging others seemed more appealing at the time). Now, you might be wondering why that's such a short amount of time, given that people are entrusting me with their health. Sure, I'd be wondering that too. However, here's the scariest thought…

As of November 2021, you can become a Level Three qualificd pcrsonal traincr, thc required qualification to be called a 'personal trainer' in just three weeks. (Level Two is a 'fitness instructor' who can only show you how to use a machine). I don't know what's more worrying – the companies that facilitate this madness, the governing body that allows this (oh yeah, there isn't one), or the trainers who exploit it. I mean, education is important, but big biceps are 'importanter', right?

Qualified, it was time to make a career as a personal trainer. With the qualification, came my ego. This is not uncommon for those who have just qualified, we think we know EVERYTHING, and I'm not just talking about fitness:

'Do you know how to change a spark plug?'

Sure, I'm a Qualified PT.

'Have you ever heard about the symbology in the DaVinci artwork?'

Sure, I'm a Qualified PT.

'Do you know what the square root of 639 is?'

Sure, I'm a Qualified PT. Now,ask me how much I can bench.

As a personal trainer, you're basically Jesus in Lycra. You can walk on water, turn water to wine, part the Red Sea, slam a revolving door, and count to infinity… twice. Confidence is just part of the job, I guess.

It's no surprise to me that we have such a high turnover of trainers in the fitness industry. The urge to leave the club is as strong as the urge to join it. The reality is that we only know a fraction of what's out there. Good personal trainers always learn on the job. It's a never-ending lesson where each and every client teaches you something you did or didn't want to know. My education resulted in my first qualified job at a well-known 'Celebrity' PT studio in Hampstead, north London in 2010.

Oh yeah, here's another thing. We snooty personal trainers don't call our places of work 'gyms' —'those are for the commoners —'we call them 'studios' as it sounds fancier.

It was here where I landed my first big celebrity client and my first glimpse into the more 'exclusive' circles. It was back in the day when the term 'celebrity trainer' was the equivalent of being an airline pilot of the seventies – it had kudos, prestige. Nowadays, a blue tick and over 20,000 followers will get you some form of celebrity status.

I worked at this studio for three years and cut my teeth on some of the most high profile celebrities (A to F list) and billionaires in the city, which I will tell you about later in this chapter.

Ironically, so many personal trainers desperately want to train a celebrity, as if it's a badge of honour, or access into the higher echelons of the fitness society. The truth is, celebrities rarely want to pay (because Judas down the road will do it for free), they never turn up, and most do it sporadically to fall in line with a new album, TV show or a film that they're hawking. And you'll rarely ever get the shout out you deserve because real celebrities require you to sign lethal NDAs. What I will say is that in those three years I met some of the most colourful characters I've ever met. I also had to pay my dues to some of the worst people I've ever had the displeasure of meeting, but that's life.

Above all, however, was the treasured business experience I would gain. I was given access to the inner workings of what seemed to be a pretty well-established professional health and fitness business, but it didn't take me long to realise that these guys were some of the biggest charlatans in this industry. They had monopolised the London market with boutique luxury studios by getting on board a very deep-pocketed investor with no real competition.

(As a side note: planning permission on gyms in London is incredibly hard to get. You are either forced to work for someone, find big investment or run a tiny outfit with lowish overheads).

With a huge budget for PR and marketing it was a recipe for success, or should I say, perceived success.

But soon the smokescreen slipped, and the reality was all too clear for anyone who worked there. Yeah, there were celebrities, but the dismal wage we were on (well under the average London wage, plus £3 was added per client as 'commission') led to a very disgruntled workforce. Never in all my years as a personal trainer have I worked somewhere that was so negative, so badly managed and so poorly paid. It bred hateful personal trainers who would only look out for themselves and that negativity would seep out onto the clients. Unsurprisingly, it wasn't long before the company fell into disrepute.

But, as much as I have a personal disdain for the owners, I have to say that they gave me the start that I needed, so I am eternally grateful. Those awful mornings working the graveyard shifts, taking the pain-in-the-ass clients that no one else wanted to train, not having scheduled breaks and the training sessions I sacrificed, all led me to building a client base that saw me travel the world, teach me the rights and wrongs of a successful PT business of my own, and above all gave me the stories and memories that fill this book.

So, for your viewing pleasure I'm going to start with my first celebrity client/friend, who I shall call – L.

SAVING RYAN'S PRIVATES

I t was a beautiful hot day in June 2010 when I found myself in a rather uncomfortable position by a male client. For the sake of this story, I'll call him 'L'.

L was a well-known singer in the music industry. He had a ferocious cocaine habit and a libido that was equally as debauched. We got on well; he was achieving pretty good results (when he wasn't hungover) and his career was on the rise. Most of you out there in the UK will definitely know the band he fronted. We became close over the summer, and he'd often invite me out for drinks with 'the boys' or to attend a gig, or an after party that he and his friends were throwing. I rarely ever accepted (I'd be up at 4.30am almost every morning) and I always thought that going out mid-week was for the rich or the jobless, or – in his case – an over-indulging celebrity. Alas, this one time he caught me off guard.

I was newly single, which L took great delight in, so he invited me for a night out with a 'few familiar faces' he knew.

'Fuck it, why not,' was my ignorantly blissful response. It wasn't often you were invited go out with a world-famous singer.

This was my first mistake.

Now, before I enlighten you to L's world, it's worth mentioning that if you've never been to London in the summer then you're missing out. Hot summers in London are always sensational. People relax, the mood is upbeat, post 5pm the bars are crammed wall-to-wall with gorgeous people, and everyone is high on spirits. It's a pretty awesome place to be, especially if you have a sex drive like a mating rabbit, have endless funds and have wide-eyed fans throwing themselves at you because of your fame.

So, here was the deal. I'd get a taxi over to L's pad at around 8pm. I'd have a few drinks and keep it simple. He on the other hand would sink a bottle of vodka, snort too many ivory lines, shoot 16 shots, neck four cans of lager with four or five chasers, and that was just for starters. Then we'd hook up with the rest of his band in some pub in Camden.

From there on out, it was anyone's game.

What could go wrong?

I had never been to L's flat. In fact, I had never been to any of my clients' houses yet. It was early in my career, and I was employed to work in a studio so there was no real need to do any home training. That was to come. I also didn't make it a habit of mine to socialise with clients, but on this odd, out of character evening, I had found myself pressing the buzzer on the large black cast iron gate that adorned the front of L's apartment block to be let upstairs.

L lived in a beautiful penthouse apartment that overlooked King's Cross. It was stunning. The whole flat was open plan with views that gave your eyes an orgasm. The beautiful low sunset cast its orange glow over the London skyline, making the apartment feel like it was giving you a reassuring hug. Precariously placed artwork littered the open brickwork walls. A DJ booth sat comfortably in one corner of the room giving off a low-level chill-hop house sound that immediately made you feel at ease. Another corner of the flat hosted the open plan kitchen and dining area where the copper taps and dark marble surfaces glistened in the evening light. Beautiful reclaimed oak planks made up the flooring with selected bits of ultra-modern furniture that were placed at odd angles to offset the never-ending sheets of slightly green tinted glass that surrounded the apartment. White linen canopies draped effortlessly over the vaulted wooden beams like ballerinas in dance. This place was beyond unreal.

Now, all would have been well if I was on my own. But I wasn't, I was with L and his degenerate associates and hangers-ons; it was only a matter of time before chaos would descend on the evening.

Upon my arrival, L opened the large metal lift door and greeted me in what I can only describe as a female geisha sarong. Here we go, I thought.

'Alright, Hugh Hefner?' I said mocking his ridiculous attire.

'You prick, get in here,' he winked, ushering me into the spacious living room.

This dude was never alone, so it shouldn't have surprised me to find the penthouse littered with people all engulfed in their own little worlds.

Two dreadlocked dudes huddled by the DJ booth, one with a set of headphones on his ear like he was trying to decipher Morse Code and the other carefully skinning a joint whilst he simultaneously looked through his record bag.

Three good-looking girls with pretentious piercings and wanky tattoos – you know the type – sat on top of the kitchen surface eating crisps and drinking some concoction from a lurid red pitcher.

Two girls were over by one of the windows looking at the view. One was completely naked, and I mean, COMPLETELY naked. She also had the most incredible dragon tattoo that started from the centre of her back and flowed effortlessly down to her slim milky white waist, finally wrapping around her ankle. Remember this woman, for she will be the catalyst of this story – and for the weirdest night out I've ever had.

A further two people were making out on one of the loungers. I couldn't tell what sex they were. It looked like two hairy beavers wrestling on a chaise longue, to be honest.

On every table there was enough bugle to kill a brass band.

There was a rabble of people outside on one of the balconies fighting over whose turn it was to get a toke on the potent weed they were smoking. Albeit a beautiful place, you couldn't get away from the sickly-sweet musty smell of the evil 'erb.

And then it hit me.

Right there, kicking back on one of the couches, as happy as pig in shit, and in clear view of everyone in the flat was a heavyweight in the acting industry – one of the most famous actors in the world – who, for the sake of this story, I'll call 'Hollywood'. Two girls sat either side of him. Again, both completely naked. He too, was wearing one of these geisha robes.

Nothing weird about this situation. Nothing at all.

Whilst this came as a surprise that this guy was here, it took me a second to realise what the hell was going on. It was like my head was playing table tennis. Titties to the left, Hollywood the net, titties to the right. I didn't know what, or who, to look at first.

'Come on soppy bollocks, let's get you a drink,' L said as he wrapped his arm around my shoulder, moving me towards the kitchen.

I couldn't help but be a tiny bit star struck by the figure on the sofa. 'Whaaa thaaa faaaack, is that who I think it is?' I said in astonishment.

'Yeah, mate, absolute legend, proper nice guy, really funny, top bloke, sweet dude,' he said as he paused to take out a small glass vial from his pocket and snorted up the contents.

'Who are all these chicks, dude?' I asked.

'Just some locals,' sniff-sniff 'Knock yourself out, Matty.'

I looked around taking in my surroundings. 'Na, I'm alright thanks, pal.'

'You pussy!' L fired back with a lopsided wink.

It took me a while to settle. I chased as many beers as I could in as little time as possible. If there's one thing to do in social situations that are awkward it's just drink until you forget it's awkward. Works a treat.

Half an hour in and one of the girls from the kitchen had taken a liking to me, because in her words I was 'strangely normal' and was feeding me what I can only describe as potent piss water from the red pitcher that the other girls were drinking from. I needed to be on some form of level with this lot, so I was going for broke. Plus, she was crazy hot.

This was my second mistake.

More and more women were turning up at the penthouse, some wearing clothes, some barely covered. It was obvious that these girls preferred to do their work at night, if you catch my drift. The front door was a revolving entry point for misfits, familiar-looking fashionistas and high-profile hipsters from the music scene who were arriving en masse with their dodgy looking security, who seemingly were also their own personal drug dealers.

A couple of hours passed and the night was in full swing; the music had turned from chill into an all-out ear-splitting rave, and observing through bleary eyes, the rest of the famous band arrived fashionably late. Too late to leave for the shit pub in Camden, thank God. This was now a full-on house party lock-in and no-one was allowed to leave.

The hot girl from the kitchen who had made a beeline for me had now become disinterested in my normalness and decided to simply pass out next to me. To drown my sorrows, I decided to carry on drinking the alcoholic piss smoothie.

This was my third mistake.

I, also, passed out.

It felt as though I had only been out for five minutes, but I woke up realising that not only was it now two in the morning, but the partitioning doors had been closed, dividing the apartment into two. All that was left on my side was a DJ who seemed as if he hadn't moved and a few people sprawled out on the couches, comatose and naked.

I, on the other hand, couldn't move.

My limbs were like lead. It was like I had been tied to the couch at every extremity. I was still aware of what was going on, but for the life of me I couldn't move my arms, my legs, and most importantly, my neck. My head was stuck in one position but I could still see the girl who had been force-feeding me the cocktail. She was still passed out but now she was also naked.

What the hell had happened? Had she got too hot and

stripped off in her comatose state? Had someone taken advantage of her? It wasn't me, was it?

I was now shitting myself, trying to find solace in the fact that I was still dressed. I knew I was too wasted to take anything off, or put it back on for that matter, so I knew I wouldn't be going to jail in the morning. The thought scared the shit out of me, so I knew I had to try and leave this place before something serious happened. The problem was I still couldn't move.

In my fruitless attempts to wake up, I tried to blink my eyes as many times as possible to get some clarity. I realised that the only option left was to let the strange sensation wash over me. Give in.

Just as I slowly grew used to the idea that I was actually OK – I hadn't pissed myself yet – and I most definitely hadn't abused anyone, a huge crash woke everyone from their slumber in the room I was in.

Suddenly one of the band members came hurtling through the partition in the wall, and skidded on the wooden floor, like a cowboy being thrown out of a saloon. He got up looking like a small gnome ready for a punch-up when L appeared, fully naked, screaming at him about something unintelligible. People were now shouting, glasses were being smashed, and the band member was now in a full-on argument with L – with everyone watching. Within seconds, more people appeared from the other side of the partition, all wearing robes, trying to break up the argument. The naked girl with the dragon tattoo seemed like she was in full control and ushered the band member out of the front door.

The night had gone from weird to all out mental, and not only that, it seemed that I had caught a case of Lashington's Disease, so completely fucked that at any given moment you could quite easily piss yourself without any restraint. However, to my relief, my body was now gradually understanding that it had motor control and I could finally bring myself up from the slump I'd been in the last few hours.

At this point I noticed that the partition had actually been separating what I later discovered to be a full-on orgy. One that I was clearly invited to but had missed out because of the strangely dead-looking girl next to me.

L, seeing that I was now in the land of living, promptly came and sat next to me, pushing the comatose girl's legs out the way, leaving her to gradually slide off the sofa.

Thud.

I looked over and saw that the fall hadn't woken her, even though she'd just headbutted the floor.

'Shouldn't we make surrrre she'sss OK, duuude?' I asked L, realising my speech hadn't quite caught up with the rest of my mouth.

'What happened to you, bro?' he chuckled. 'You been drinking what she's been drinking?' pointing to the she-zombie on the floor and the red pitcher next to her.

'Yeeehhhh, brrrrooooooooo. What wasss in that shiiyaat?'

'Donkey Dust, Vitamin K… you know, Ketamine,' he replied. 'Listen, you can't tell anyone about what's happened tonight, OK, this shit stays with us. That dickhead's probably going to go and blab to the press now I've kicked him out the band.'

'Why, whaatss happpthhened?'

At that very moment the chick with the dragon tattoo appeared, draped herself over L, and started whispering into his ear.

'Gotta go, buddy, I've gotta sort this one out,' he said as he tapped me on the knee before nodding to the dragon chick.

I can only imagine what he meant. It was time to go. At that point, the drugs were wearing off, so I had a little look around for some water and grabbed a taxi and took myself home. It was enough madness for one night. I was done.

It must be noted I have a pretty high tolerance to alcohol but I'm not a drug user. The closest thing I've ever got to a Class A is taking codeine after an injury. This night fucked me up, but it was the days after that were truly horrific – a proper comedown. Man, I felt terrible. All the muscles in my body ached as if I'd run a marathon. I felt so emotionally drained that anything could have sent me into puddles of tears. I even cried at *Songs of Praise*.

Remember kids – Drugs are bad mmmmkay.

It took me a week to get back to normal again. Sure, I cried myself to sleep for the first five days but the show had to go on. I hadn't seen or spoken to L because he'd cancelled the sessions, and, frankly, I didn't feel like seeing or talking to anyone. This wouldn't be the last time I felt like this either.

The following week, L was booked in for a session.

Blissfully unaware and acting like nothing had ever happened, L came bouncing into the studio like a Gummy Bear on speed. However, he was limping, and wincing every time he took a step down the stairs.

'How you feeling, son? You OK now?' he asked.

'No, mate, I'm not, in fact I'm pretty much definitely not OK. My body feels like it's been through Jamie Oliver's blender. Every time I try and have a wank all I can think about is the face of the naked girl-zombie on your floor. I'm ruined boss, ruined.'

'Hahaaaa chillout, Matty, you just got on "one",' L laughed. 'Listen, no great story ever came from eating a salad. You need to let your hair down more. The girl's fine, pal. All in a day's work for her, that's what she's paid for.' He then went on to explain to me the turn of events that had left me lying in bed for a week thinking about world peace, Bob Geldof and how I could save dolphins.

It turned out that the night had started with just a few friends over, but L had found out that his actor buddy 'Hollywood' was in town and so he invited him over, knowing full well that that was an open invite to get any women they wanted. As I previously mentioned, L was a sex addict, so any opportunity to have copious amounts of women around him wasn't turned down. And that's when I arrived. The 'party' was just gearing up, hence the naked women and the drugs. I'd unfortunately been taken out of action early on, as I had found myself in the sky of diamonds with Lucy, missing out on the celebrity orgy that had then transpired. Apparently, this is quite common. Or at least it was with this band.

The reason that it had all kicked off was because the band member who had been kicked out, had got a little too 'friendly' with L's on-off dragon tattoo girlfriend.

'The dickhead only played drums anyway, he's easily replaceable,' L said of why the sacking hadn't made the front page of the *Sun*.

'Just a normal night for you hey, kid?' I asked. Fuck it, I thought. I'll scrub this one down as a learning curve.

Back to the session.

'Matty, can we do something else, this rower's giving me nut ache?' L asked.

'What's up?' I ask, remembering that L was limping.

'I just want to do something else, mate, I'm a little bit fragile, you know… down there,' pointing to his nether regions.

I could see that he was squirming uncomfortably, knowing he was going to have to confess his ailments to Dr Hodges.

And then it happened. Those words I'll never forget – 'Can I show you something, mate?' L said sheepishly. 'Honest you won't laugh.'

'Sure, sure,' I reassured him while knowing full well that if there's something to laugh at, I will. I manoeuvred him over to a part of the studio far away from prying eyes.

I must tell you that it isn't uncommon to be told of a client's body and health issues and their numerous ailments. In fact, I encourage it. I have come face to face with psoriasis, gout, gum disease and had to handle numerous mental health obscurities.

However, what was to follow was a first for me. Without any hesitation, L dropped his drawers and proceeded to pull his 'mini boy' out for perusal.

'Avert your eyes, ladies,' I shouted, embarrassed that I now had to look at his penis. I glanced, trying to look, but not directly in the eye, as it were. I glance again. Wait…

'WHAT THE FUCK HAS HAPPENED TO YOU???!?!'

'Shut up you divvy, don't let everyone know,' L fired back, as he looked down holding his shirt up with his chin. 'She bloody got me, didn't she?! The chick you met with the bloody tattoo, you know the dragon one, she fucked me up good and proper this time.'

'Jesus, what did she have, a wood cutter for a fanny? You could sieve spaghetti with that.'

I was still trying to figure out what bit was actually attached to the body. His manhood was swollen all shades of red and it looked like a toadstool that had been decimated by a forest fire. I'm now pointing at this gargoyle of a thing.

'L, you always need to cover your stump before you hump pal. You're in serious trouble.'

'I know that you fucking prick, what am I going to do? What do you think it is?' he asked.

'What do I think it is? Well, it's certainly not human that's for sure, it looks like roadkill.'

Luckily, he saw the bright side to it all, and put his mogwai back in its box. Apparently ol' dragon tattoo had a penchant for 'aggressive sex' but that night things got out of hand and L was left with a nasty case of what I now like to call Freddie Kruger's pinky'. It's always funny until someone gets hurt... and then it's hilarious. I couldn't let it lie.

'Mate, that looks like someone's tried to play the harmonica with your manhood. You give a new definition to playing the pink Oboe, that's for sure.'

L stood there wincing in pain as he collected his things together, looking none too impressed. I told him to see a doctor immediately because he needed antibiotics. He appreciated the advice. But I couldn't help one last dig.

'Well, look on the bright side, bro, at least you've found your new band member.'

It's been years since I've seen or spoken to L, but in that time frame the band disappeared into the shadows much like a lot of those manufactured groups of the Noughties. I'm absolutely sure he's still out there ravaging his way through bowls of ivory powder, organising debauchery, fraternising with Hollywood royalty (that guy is still mega famous by the way) and dealing with grotesque self-inflicted war wounds. While I'm glad I'm not now witnessing infected twig and giggleberries, I do miss L and the camaraderie we used to have. Celebrities are a funny bunch – you're about to witness two more of them in fact – but L truly was one in a million.

Wherever you are pal, a word of advice. 'Next time – cloak the joker before you poke her.'

THE MAYOR

Let me tell you about a faraway land called Knobsville, a place that houses the infamous clan of Knobbers. It's in a not so well-known area called Knob-On-Sea, in the county of Knobsfordshire, which sits comfortably on the Isle of Knob.

The person I'm about to tell you about is actually the Mayor of Knobsville.

It wasn't long after I started to train L that I came into contact with my second major celebrity while working at the boutique north London studio. Whilst many of us PTs at the studio were new to the industry, it was at a time when having a celebrity as a client was similar to winning the lottery, so we were all hot on each others' heels trying to pitch to win the client. Never one to miss out, I put my bid in for the next client, which meant a verbal version of my limited CV embellished to buggery making me look like I'd written the personal training curriculum … and, lo and behold, he, the celebrity, chose me.

Let it be known that when you start with a new celebrity client it takes a good few sessions to find your rhythm and an equal amount of time to find a nice balance between your two personalities and sense of humour, just as it does a 'normal' person. You have your clients who you can say 'fuck' and 'bugger' to, and then there are the others where you wouldn't dare be so informal. On this occasion, I found it hard to strike the balance. Not because the client was awkward or shy, but because I quickly found myself at the butt of their jokes instead.

The client was a famous comedian, so I thought this only normal, and having spent the last year being surrounded by the likes of Danger and Irish, I wasn't scared of having a new arsehole ripped open for me, figuratively speaking, of course.

But his ridiculing me was just a little too early, a little too harsh and a little bit … well, inappropriate for someone who had only known me for a brief amount of time. Mum jokes are fine. But perhaps not on the first session.

'What's Mrs Hodges's name?' he asked within the first twenty minutes.

'Why?' I replied.

'It's always good to know the names of someone's parents just in case there's an emergency. If you were to trip and fall over this dumbbell, who would I call?' he said jokingly, with his smarmy tone. 'I bet she's called Alice, isn't she? A fucking Alice, the most droll name out there, haha,' he laughed.

My back is up. If he goes where I think he's going to go, then I'm not going to be the one who trips over the dumbbell. Not today, Satan.

And then out of nowhere, he broke into song:

'Twenty four years just waiting for a chance,
To tell her how I feel,
And maybe get a second glance,
Now I've got to get used to not living next door to Alice,
Alice, who the FUCK is Alice?'

And it was at this point that the verse would be sung in sporadic fashion mid-session, whenever he felt like bringing up the idea of taking the piss out of my mum, just to keep me on edge. For the record, she isn't even called Alice.

OK, it might not sound much. And, I thought, no harm, no

foul, I could take it. Millions knew him to be a great comedian, but so far, I thought he was about as funny as what L had on his dick.

But it wasn't this that got me. It was this precise charade that would be acted out every session. The act. The constant throwing his towel at me like he was playing in a Wimbledon final, or demands I bring him cold water and then burping loudly on me, in my face. Everything he did was done in order to get my attention. It was weird.I have friends who are comedians and they are often troubled souls, quiet, and avoiding the limelight, but this guy loved every second of it. Every moment of every session was a chance to perform, or take the piss out of me, or just be plain rude. And it wasn't just me, everyone in the studio got some form of abuse for no other reason other than his own cruel entertainment.

During one session he turned to one of my bespectacled female colleagues, and said, 'You must be excited for 2020?'

'Why?' the trainer replied.

'Well, because it'll be first time you'll have seen 20-20, you four-eyed specky bogglin.'

He was just being mean. He didn't know the trainer; he was just showing off in front of the other clients who, by the way, saw him for what he was – a first-grade dicksplash.

His tenure as the Mayor of Nobsville was about to be toppled, however.

On the day of reckoning I was feeling less patient than normal (which, by the way, is pretty low bar at the best of times), so I decided that it would only be fair if one of my colleagues were to take the burden and train The Mayor that day. It was an easy sell because there's nothing like the sound of extra commission to sway a PT.

I was about to get sweet, sweet revenge too.

Given that the studio had quite a prestigious reputation in the right circles, we'd often be graced with people who'd come in for the odd session or two when they were travelling. This time, after I had skilfully palmed off The Mayor, I was appointed a perfectly pleasant, quiet gentleman from New York who had flown over for his niece's bat mitzvah party at Nobu, in Mayfair.

Our usual schtick was to put each client on a piece of cardio equipment to 'walk and talk', so that we could get a better picture as to what the client wanted and needed from that session.

Let me paint an important picture for you here. The studio floor was formed in the shape of a long L and was more than 3,000 square feet. One side of the L was the cardio equipment, mats and mobility area, whereas on the other side of the L was the resistance equipment.

The Mayor was in the resistance area with my colleague, chewing his ear off about this and that, heavily animated as ever and spinning a load of bullshit. I was standing next to our New York friend on the treadmill who proceeded to tell me about the event that he had attended for his niece in London the night before. This guy was a big Jewish heavyweight in the commercial property sector in Manhattan, and his family who lived in London were equally heavyweight. A lot of money had gone into this bat mitzvah. *A lot.* They'd even hired a famous comedian…

You can see where this is going, right?

Got it in one.

They'd hired The Mayor.

So, I took it upon myself, like anyone would in this situation, to question our New York neighbour about what he thought of The Mayor, knowing that he was, in fact, just around the corner.

'Oh, he was great, but boy does he suffer from nerves. He nearly didn't come and perform. His management tried to call it off, but we insisted on paying him more,' he replied.

'Wow, that's unusual. So, what does one have to pay for something like that?' I ask.

'Thirty-grand for an hour,' he replied nonchalantly.

Thirty fucking grand.

For an hour.

I ignore this ridiculous amount of money and push more on his nervousness. 'So he suffers from nerves, huh? I would never have known. You know we train him here, he always seems really confident,' I said, grinning on the inside.

'Oh, yeah, like a lot. I had to go talk to him backstage, calm his nerves.'

At this very point, I shit you not, on the other side of the studio, The Mayor started talking loudly about the bat mitzvah from the night before and got louder and louder until everyone in the gym was listening intently ... including my client from New York. You couldn't help but hear his thundering voice.

'Can you fucking believe it, John, they paid me thirty fucking grand for an hour, thirty FUCKING GRAND! I've never done an easier gig!' he scoffed. 'What mug pays thirty fucking grand for an hour, John?' he continued.

This. Is. Awesome, I thought. My skin was excitedly itching knowing something was about to go off between The Mayor and Mr New York.

So I did what any reasonable person would do in this situation, and turned the treadmill down, so Mr New York could hear everything.

'And not only that, John, they've asked me to do another bat mitzvah for the same rate. That's the kids' school fees paid!' he carried on boasting, unknowing he now had the studio's full attention.

I looked at my client, Mr New York. He looked at me. His face was filling up with rage.

'Can you hold on for a second, please?' he said stopping the treadmill mid-walk.

'Be my guest, sir,' I smugly replied, bowing my head, ushering him with a rolling arm towards the imminent storm.

He stepped down off the machine, calmly walked over to The Mayor, who had no idea Mr New York was there that day.

Here I was in the background motioning to my colleague to pay attention, because shit was about to go down. I took a ringside seat on the nearby spin bike ready for what was about to happen. All I needed was a supersized Diet Coke and a bucket of salted popcorn.

Mr New York approached the joker like a lioness stalking her prey. The Mayor was locked in his gunsight, blood was about to be spilled, jokes were about to fall on a flat audience; the death of a comedian was imminent. 3D glasses at the ready … we were about to witness a murder.

The Mayor's normal plump red cheeks drained faster than the toes of a Reynaud's sufferer. The wild, boastful gesticulations stopped. The whole studio was silent, and The Mayor knew he was about to get a very public dressing down.

'Hello again,' Mr New York said calmly. 'I couldn't help but overhear what you were saying.'

The Mayor started stuttering, his embarrassment was priceless. 'B,b,b, but, I, I, I, yes hello, ummm I, I, I, sorry but but…'

Mr New York turned to address the rest of the studio. Must have been at least twenty people standing still. It was as if a scene from a *Poirot* episode, where he addressed his audience to make his final statement, had come to life.

'As you see fit to mock my family, let it be known that you were petrified of performing last night. And may I remind you that it took a number of us to get you on stage. You will not be performing for my family again – say goodbye to that next bat mitzvah …'

With that, my client turned his back on The Mayor. The level of awkward reached epic levels.

I was loving every minute of it.

I shared an awkward glance with The Mayor.

He knew.

Payback.

It came as no surprise that The Mayor didn't train at the studio again, but I couldn't care less. The Mayor of Nobsville had had his final comeuppance.

Mazel Tov, baby!

THE BILLION DOLLAR NOSE JOB

I t's funny when I look back at the likes of L and The Mayor, and the times when having someone with some form of status meant everything as a personal trainer. Fifteen years on and it all becomes a bit of a blur. I don't know how many celebrities, or high net worth clients I've trained over the years, but I can tell you that the overall sessions number must be in the tens of thousands. I no longer get star struck, so training a celebrity or someone who is considered a mega player in the fame and fortune business doesn't really light a fire inside me anymore. When you realise the realities of what these sort of clients can mean – rarely turning up, slow results, unproductive sessions and insulting or derogatory experiences that leave you stressed as hell, you construct a numbness to that person's status. There are those, however, who do stick in your mind. The following client is a good example of the celebrity mindset/manipulation of the personal trainer's need to please and serve. When your income is never guaranteed on a day-to-day basis, you will do anything to retain the continued business.

I jump forward two years to an early 2012 Autumn

morning. I'd been at the same studio for a while now and had grown a strong client list.

The day started well. I wasn't on an early shift, so I had about as much sleep as I could possibly get from finishing at 10pm the previous night and starting at 9am the following morning. The birds were singing in the trees, a light breeze whistled through the streets, green and brown leaves fell through the air like falling feathers. Early autumn conkers had started to fall, littering the pavement like spiky green hedgehogs. The smell of damp grass emanated from the lawns of local gardens, whilst the sun shone brightly glistening off the edges of car mirrors from the gentle trundling cars that passed by, blinding the local walkers. Today was going to be a good day, I thought.

However…

Like most of the days that I had come accustomed to, days like these tended not to end the way that they started, so I was more than prepared for the 'Fuckening', a term I've coined to describe when your day is too good to be true for it not to become totally fucked by the end. And to my 'not so' surprise, today was to be no different.

Upon arriving at the studio, I was greeted by my then-manager who was in a frantic tizzy about a new mega-wealthy VIP client, a client whose urine turned to wine, a client who was so influential that it was imperative that they were given a first-class service, a client – who, even without meeting them, had already irritated me.

This client was important to the manager. It was on me to train her.

Well, it didn't take long before the client presented herself to us all, with six bodyguards in tow. It took me a while to recognise who she was, due to her hiding behind a thick mink three-quarter-length coat and huge dark sunglasses that masked her petite face. Even behind the mask you could see that this girl had had recent cosmetic surgery, but whatever, this was Hampstead – who hadn't?

I made my introduction and guided her into the gym whilst her bodyguards left through the front door and patrolled outside.

While going through the rigmarole of her taking her death coat off, I explained what it was that we were doing that day. The studio had set parameters that every new client must complete before training begins, an orientation as it were, which had been designed as more of a sales pitch than anything else. I could tell already that this was going to be another case of 'weights are bad for women', 'women shouldn't lift over two kilograms' kinda client (aka the 'I don't want to build too much muscle' brigade), so the cardio area was to be stage one of Project Billionaire, as I coined her. She hadn't said much but, as expected, she was pleased that we were leaving the 'scary' weights section.

What does this woman look like, I hear you ask? Think Posh Spice but proper posh, slightly older, ten times wealthier, and stacked with more diamonds than Rick Ross on a spending spree in Hatton Garden, plus a body that all Instagrammers would kill for, and a nose that I can only describe as … Michael Jacksonesque. It was so strange – perfectly elfish – but it turned her face into something that was more like a doll than a human. Anyway, she was in a different league altogether. And her nose showed the world that she clearly had more money than sense.

Most people can handle walking in a straight line. Well, let me tell you – this woman couldn't. Something was up, for sure. During any first session, it's my job to analyse a client's biomechanics and gait. This girl was just off the scale; think Phoebe from *Friends* running (YouTube: Phoebe's run). Normally, when someone's gait is crooked it's at least consistently crooked. Our billionaire friend here was the exception to the rule. She ran like she was trying to flick shit off her shoe. There was something off, so I probed a bit deeper with a brief medical diagnosis and report.

Medical reports are essential for every trainer to cover their asses from getting sued if/when something goes wrong. Example questions are mundane. 'Have you, or any of your immediate family suffered any heart attacks in the last five years?' Or 'Do you have any bone or joint problems, made worse by exercise?'

You get the idea. However, this was my perfect opportunity to find out what the hell was going on between her ears, so I veered off from the script in front of me.

'Are you on any medication that would affect what we do today?' I asked suspiciously.

I waited for the answer.

A resounding no.

OK, I don't believe you ... so ...

'Are you taking any medication that affects your balance or makes you tired?'

She ignored this question whilst aimlessly staring out the window. After a few seconds, when she realized I was still talking to her, she nodded in the affirmative.

Suddenly, I had a feeling I knew what was going on.

'Are those anti-depressants you're taking making you into a space cadet who can't control their legs?'

Joke – I didn't ask her that, but I wish I could have. I'd had a similar experience with a client a year earlier where they'd admitted to taking anti-depressants, which massively inhibited their performance, so I had learned how to spot the signs.

'Are you currently taking any SSRI's or anti-depressants?' I asked.

She replied with an immediate but quiet 'Yes'.

Gotcha. Time to come off the old treadmill, bandy legs.

The rest of the session was pretty formulaic in nature but there was something about this client that was intriguing. It wasn't the fact that her visual appearance was so strange, or the fact that she constantly looked like she was looking down on everyone (although she definitely was); it was more that she was completely off the wall *wacky*. I liked her, she was unusual, and there was definitely more to her than met the eye. I'd like to say that I chose to train her, but the reality was that she was assigned to me over the next ten weeks, so I didn't really have a choice.

The sessions that followed were slow going but she was starting to show her true colours. Some days she would be bouncing off the walls, others she would be back in her galactic spaceship away with the stars. On those days it was like trying to herd cats, so I'd already given up on the session before it had started. However, there were those days where she would be lucid, and her personality started to shine through and the real person started to emerge. On the days when she hadn't downed half a bottle of Diazepam she would be gossiping about this celebrity or that celebrity who she knew, the premieres, high-class functions and elite events she'd attended, the 'ghastly awful' staff she had to put up with or the people in her life who couldn't keep up with her lifestyle, or, more importantly, the surgeon who had messed up her nose the last time she visited (more about this later). Some people would call this bitching, but, knowing her, I called it 'verbal anger therapy', and it is common in my trade. As mundane as verbal anger therapy can be, you always have to keep the client happy and positive, but you also have to be mindful that you don't get dragged down to that level.

That said, she used to bring her dog into the sessions, which was fine by me. Put a suitcase next to me with a thousand pounds in it or show me a puppy and I'm choosing the doggo any day of the week. My own puppy, Honey, was the apple of my eye, so I always thought that it doesn't matter how much of a dick you are, if you love dogs, you are Kool And The Gang with me. She soon realised my love for our canine friends when I regularly suggested that we break up the monotony of the sessions to take her, her six bodyguards and her puppy onto Hampstead Heath for some fresh air. She knew full well that this was just a guise so I could walk the dog, but she never seemed to mind and relished in the fact she hadn't had to lift any weights in that session. But, more importantly, it was because she wanted to offload her issues onto me.

Suddenly, I became her consort, a kind of hairdresser, someone who she could just offload onto without any interruptions.

And here lies an important observation of the rich and famous. Throughout my career I have noticed that the majority of these people are desperately unhappy. I joke that our billionaire friend's idea of happiness is a Hermes bag and a bottle of Prozac, but the reality is that they are not fulfilled in most areas of their lives. I've lost count of the number of times both male and female clients find short-term happiness through surgery, high-class escorts, drugs, alcohol, material possessions or the odd fling here and there. As the Notorious B.I.G once said, 'Mo money, mo problems,' and he was absolutely right. Being a PT isn't just about the body, it is also about the mind – and mental health is as important as body health.

Our outdoor walks were often on the subject of personal appearance and given that it was a personal training session I thought nothing of it. However, what became apparent was that these chats often turned into talks about her appearance and how it could be changed through surgery.

Trigger Alert!! I'm not a big fan of cosmetic surgery. Sure, if you're not happy with how your nose looks then get it sorted but, if you're having liposuction or getting bits chopped off because of no other reason than you're too lazy to exercise and eat properly, then I'm not going to support you.

Fortunately, it transpired that my Project Billionaire had serious issues with the way her face looked. She hated the look of her own face.

Imagine hating your own face. It's tough. And I sympathised greatly because the older you get, the less your face is for TV and more for radio.

No diet or training regime can sort that one out. She'd had, from what she told me, numerous nose surgeries but the last one was the *coup de grace*. It had now turned into a full-blown litigation process because she wasn't happy with the surgeon who was recommended to her by a friend (the same client who is the subject of 'Neighbourly Love' later in this book). It was a peculiar looking nose. She wouldn't have looked altogether out of place in *The Legend Of Zelda*.

Months passed, sessions flew by, and we were now in the thick of a relationship where I was more her counsellor than personal trainer. Her dog had multiplied by two and the bodyguards had halved. I'd grown to be somewhat indifferent to her chat because by now I was frankly bored of hearing how ugly she thought she was. Her issues with the legal proceedings in her suing her plastic surgeon were at the top of her stress list every session. Getting her nose back was her sole priority.

So, being the Samaritan that I am, I thought I'd throw her, her nose, and her dog, a bone to try and cheer her up a little bit.

Through my contacts, I had managed to be well-in with Battersea Dogs Home, who every year threw an annual fundraiser ball in London, called Collars & Coats. It was an invite-only event that attracted some of the most well-known pet-mad British celebrities. This event is hot property on the capital's social calendar. Luckily, I always got a free ticket, and was allowed to invite a few of my clients to bump up the roster with the aim that they would donate handsomely. In previous years, my table alone had generated well over £50,000 with some famous clients donating the majority of that themselves. Given that this client of mine had billions and she loved dogs, I thought it only fitting that she should be invited. She duly accepted. Hell, she even smiled at the idea.

Then came the problems.

Her security had to be detailed, other guests had to be vetted, media had to be listed, the venue had to be secured in advance, travel options were booked, dietary requests were ordered. It became a fiasco from the start. Normally most celebrities would arrive, be papped on the red carpet and then ushered inside to the VIP champagne reception accompanied by all the other faces. It wasn't a place for normal folk like me, for instance. So, she was in good company and there should have been nothing to worry about.

Until the night of the event.

I'd been waiting by the bar for about an hour. Most of the guests had arrived by now and tail-enders were coming through the doors in dribs and drabs. My client was yet to show her face and we were being told to go into the seating area. I waited another fifteen minutes, then gave up and went to sit with the rest of my table, who happened to have the most famous male model in the world, his girlfriend, an ex-swimming Olympian and her partner, and a dancer and her daughter.

Sticking out like a pair of dog's bollocks there I am on my lonesome, seated next to Mr and Mrs Nobody in the form of two empty seats. I looked, and felt, like a right Billy-fucking-no-mates.

The night was in full swing and it was obvious by now that I'd been stood up. I had stuck my neck out for this – for her – I was responsible for a lot of the headache-inducing pre-event due diligence just to make her feel more comfortable so I'd be royally embarrassed, if she just didn't turn up. I therefore took it upon myself to find one of the organisers to see what had happened as the client wasn't answering her phone. I was then told that the client had in fact turned up with her make-up artist and her own security. She took a great deal of pleasure in going up and down the red carpet getting all the press she could for her own social media image, to pump up her reputation as the squeaky-clean charity-giving icon she was. But then on entering the venue she suddenly decided that it was 'too dangerous' and left due to security concerns.

There was no donation on her part either.

She used her invite as a way to get free press.

This made my piss boil. The following weeks at our sessions, I tried to hide my hurt, but she needed to know I knew. There was no more anger therapy venting on the heath, no more gentle cardio, and there were no weights under 10kg. In those weeks she probably made the best gains she'd ever done in the last twelve months – the irony. But our time was done, and she knew it. Whereas before I would put up with her racist implications and undertones, and the constant struggle about her nose, now it just made me reel in disgust that someone who could have given so much to a worthy cause, was more interested in her own reputation than the cause itself.

So, I was done, she was done.

Six months after we had separated, I found out from another client of mine that she had failed in suing her surgeon and had promptly got another nose job with yet another surgeon to amend the work that she thought wasn't done properly in the first place. I'm not ashamed to admit I've Googled her since, and, well, for such a pretty picture, her frame remains ugly.

Woof!

PART TWO

YOUR NEEDS OVER MY NEEDS

LESSON TWO:

Never argue with an immovable object. It'll always end with you being frustrated and leave you feeling like you either want to kill yourself or kill the immovable object. And don't ever fake having Tourette's.

I t's often the case that clients come to you with their own perceived idea as to how they want their PT sessions to roll out. They have their own goals, which are obviously important, but when you see someone who wants to lose 30 pounds but are weaker than a breadstick, or someone who wants their figure to look like Margot Robbie's, but instead looks like the ripest pear in harvest season, you'll often find you meet at loggerheads.

Over the years I've met some pretty headstrong clients. Given the nature of the demographic I was working in, it was a given. These clients were often older, had been through the mill, from a generation where step aerobics was a 'thing', didn't eat carbs at night, and Bear Walks were an activity you did on your Canada vacation, not on the gym floor. Likewise, at the tail end of my PT career at the boutique studio, I started training a much younger clientele who'd find their workouts on Instagram and come in with the notion that they should be doing some single leg, Bosu ball, bicep curling, standing on their head bullshit, whilst drinking a soya latte chased down with a spinach and lychee goji berry shit shot. To say I had to deal with pre-conceived notions was an understatement. The majority of my first sessions with clients were a re-education, asking them to trust the professional in front of them, and not rely on their own research. You need to think and act fast in this game. Getting someone to reach their goals is a fine mix of balancing many aspects of training, nutrition and lifestyle choices. It's hard and can often lead to dead ends. It takes two to tango, remember.

And with this in mind, being a PT can be somewhat like trying to push a boulder up a mountain, or more aptly put, pushing a fat kid out of the cake shop. You need to know when it's time to quit the battle between your client's needs and your own. If you can't find the balance, then you're either not doing a good job of listening or the war is not yours to fight, no matter how much you want to help them.

Most of the time PTs hang on to clients even though they know they're not going to achieve results. This is for a multitude of reasons. Some clients end up as friends, some need you to just 'be there' for them, and some are nothing but income. It's an unfortunate reality that most PTs hate losing clients because they know it's hard to find new ones, and in this game, word of mouth is king. When you lose a client, you lose a revenue stream. But there are times when you simply need to call a spade a spade and cut your losses.

Which is awkward for me, because I'm terrible at goodbyes.

So, I've always concocted some awful exercise that I convinced them they needed in order to 'progress' because I didn't have the nuts to tell it to them straight. After a week of demoralising workouts and the 'Do we really have to do this exercise?' whinge, you can be sure that by week three, said client would be making excuses and you'd not have to call it quits, they'd do it for you.

Or, as I have also done, take a more devious route.

This is where I will formally introduce to you the angriest, most hateful, in your face PT I've ever had the pleasure of calling a friend. And I say pleasure because Kane was so unpredictable you were guaranteed a spectacle when he was around. Yes, Kane was the Putin of PTs.

A stocky, well-built boxer of a man in his thirties, Kane had seen the harder side of life, a few too many knocks to the head and he hated, and I mean *hated*, his job as a PT. How he never got arrested I do not know, but what Kane was so skilfully brilliant at was that he would tiptoe on the tightrope of inappropriate behaviour. No other PTs I know got away with how he treated his clients. Even Danger was in awe of Kane.

Let me give you an example.

It was 2013 when I left the celebrity boutique studio that had given me my first boost to my career. After three years of piss-poor pay and God-awful hours I thought I'd try something new and go it alone.

I had a decent roster of heavyweight clients, some of whom stayed loyal, so I started looking for studios that were taking on freelance trainers. At the time, this was a pretty big move. I had a stable income that was about to be challenged and a new environment that existing clients – especially well-known ones – had to get used to. Not only had they had to acclimatise to a new studio, but they also had to get used to new trainers being around them. For all you aspiring PTs out there, I cannot stress how important the latter is to your business. If you surround yourself with idiots, you can be sure that you will be lumped into the same category.

If only I had known this back then.

Danger was by then-working at a small north London studio in St Johns Wood. The space, which was situated in a basement, was fairly small, could fit about four PTs in at one time. Water dripped from the ceiling, paint was flaking off the walls, equipment was knackered and 'motivational' *Rocky*esque quotes graced the walls. It wasn't what you'd call a studio; it was more of a crack den. I called it The Cave. Danger had invited me over and I jumped at the chance. About 30 per cent of my clients came with me but, luckily, and God knows how, this little hellhole actually pulled in some pretty wealthy, and famous punters. As grotty as it was, it still had the air of exclusivity about it.

As I came down the stairs one day, preparing myself psychologically for what might be in store, I heard Kane shouting at the top of his voice:

'YOU FAT FUCK, MOOOOVE. STOP FUCKING AROUND AND GET ON WITH IT…YOU…FAT…FUCK. IF YOU DON'T STOP WHINGING, I'll BREAK BOTH YOUR ANKLES YOU FAT FUCKING FAT FUCKER OF FATTY FUCKERS.'

Oh, here we go I thought. Fat-shaming clients was at the forefront of Kane's repertoire. Clearly no one had told him that bullying people rarely ever got the result they wanted.

I entered The Cave to find Kane standing on a female client's feet as he stood over her whilst she was doing sit-ups. The irony was that this chick was in great shape, she had less fat than an ant's nutsack.

But, oh boy, was she crying. This is NEVER a good sign in a gym.

In between sobbing, and straining her neck, Kane shouted. 'FUCKING HELL, HOW DID YOU EVER BEAT ANOREXIA, YOU FAT FUCK!'

Kane was going so hard at this poor girl, I thought she'd be eligible for mis-sold PPI protection.

Anyway, when the session seemed was over, I was fully expecting her to tell him that she never wanted to see him again, and who could blame her? But, no, instead she wiped away her tears, said it was 'the best session ever' and promptly gave him a hug and said she'd see him next time.

WHAT?

I stood there bemused at how Kane got away with this.

'Another day, another dollar,' is all Kane said as he rubbed his hands with glee.

But this wasn't Kane's piece de resistance. Once he discovered my methods of getting rid of bad clients, he was utterly unimpressed by the 'normality of it' and proceeded to tell me that not only was I chicken shit, but he would school me in the art of how to get rid of clients in a heartbeat. What he came up with is not only so outlandish that no one would even think of it, but it took some serious balls to pull it off.

The next day Kane arrived in a positive mood. He told us all to watch his session closely, because 'Matt is about to get "schooled" by a professional hate artist'. He actually said that.

I waited in anticipation for the drama to unfold.

As he gently eased his fit and good-looking client into the session, his manner was somewhat professional, he wasn't talking loudly, and the client seemed to be enjoying the non-verbal abuse that they weren't so used to. Then, suddenly, Kane bellowed:

'F-F-F-Fatty. C-C-C-C-Cock…sucker. COCKSUCKER!'

Whilst I scrambled to try to dig a black hole and bury myself in it, Kane continued on his session like nothing had happened. Five minutes later:

'Heavyweight baby. H-H-H-H-Heavyweight.'

What on earth is going on? The client looked as perplexed as we did.

'Chhhhhundermonkey.'

It then transpired that Kane had told his client that he had been diagnosed with Tourette's syndrome and that his days as a PT were numbered because of this awful disease he'd suddenly been diagnosed with. I mean, it wasn't far from the truth to be fair – Kane swore more than a pissed-up sailor.

And as you can imagine, the client never came back.

It's this kind of commitment to the cause and the sheer stubbornness of Kane that makes him so special. Not only had he lost the potential for a revenue stream – just so he could prove how much of a chicken shit I was – he actually feigned a serious illness without thinking that, at some point, the client might find out, or have friends who were also training with him who would see that, in fact, he did not suffer from Tourette's. He just didn't care.

Did I tell you he hated his job?

I challenge any client, or any personal trainer for that matter, to book any sessions in when the likes of Kane is around. Whilst it's a highly effective manoeuvre, I don't think it would be advisable to copy Kane's approach.

And anyway, how many PTs have Tourette's?

You'd never fucking get away with it.

BUNCH OF GRAPES

One of the hardest things a PT has to do is to correctly, and accurately, figure out how to deal with a client's physical limitations and issues. Whilst we aren't physios, it takes a lot of knowledge of movement patterns and physiology to prescribe a bespoke program designed for an individual client. A lot of PTs today seem to forget – or just don't know, or care – that this is a bespoke service, and not a cookie cutter, one-size-fits-all type of job.

For example, if a client presents themselves with acute ankle inversion (ankles fall inwards) through an overhead squat pattern, it's my job to know why those ankles are inverting so much and determine what action to take to strengthen/lengthen the appropriate areas so the client doesn't ultimately end up walking like John Wayne with injured knees for the rest of their life.

The story that follows is one that sticks out in my mind as one of the most unusual, because the process of finding out the issue is a story of its own, and one that baffled me for many weeks until I worked it out.

A female client came to me, to get her ready for a Grand Canyon trek she was doing the following year. Knowing she had plenty of work to do, she gave herself a good amount of time for us to make her strong. The majority of people who come to me with a notion that they need to lose weight soon realise that they need strengthening first. Fortunately, this client knew this already and wanted to jump straight into basic strength work with the barbell. Trainers love this!

The client's initial session showed no more than a few niggles here and there, some discomfort during the squat pattern and the normal adjustments to her diet. There was nothing out of the ordinary, so it should have been fairly easy going. That was until about week four where we were well into the sessions.

The client was performing something called a seated goblet squat. For those who don't know what this is, it's where you stand up and sit down onto a bench holding a dumbbell against your chest like a goblet/chalice.

We are about two repetitions into the movement, when she started complaining about the pain she experienced in the first session. Now, when someone complains of pain, the immediate question to ask is 'Where?' She was being a little elusive but said it was around 'the groin' near to the back where the sacrum (tailbone) is.

I'm thinking possible strain of hip musculature, weak glutes, adductor pressure or obturator issue, but, as I've mentioned before, I'm no physio. I lifted the weight off her and asked her to perform a body weight squat with a slightly narrower stance.

Still a lot of pain.

'What does the pain feel like?' I asked. 'Is it a dull pain, a sharp pain, a pain that feels like it could be like a trapped nerve?'

'It…it just feels like something is pulling. Like tearing almost,' she replied.

'So … a sharp pain?'

'Ah, don't worry about it, let's move on,' she replied, shutting me down.

I'll let this slide for now, I thought, but issues like this shouldn't be ignored. Pain is not something you just work through, despite what all the meathead gym rats think.

The rest of the session passed without any hiccups. The

client could perform a normal lunge pattern without discomfort, and her lower back held up in loaded positions. It was just when the client squatted, that there was this issue.

I observed that she would rarely ever take a break or sit down during rest periods. She was always on the go. I found it odd, as most clients can't wait to sit or collapse at the end of a set.

Over the next few weeks, her legs and lower back started to get stronger, so I thought I'd tempt fate and have her try some barbell squat work. The same thing happened again, but her wincing showed me that the pain was getting worse. Top marks went to this client for trying to ignore her own pain, but it was starting to niggle at me that I couldn't diagnose the problem.

The only other option was to recommend for her to go and see a physio or GP, but interestingly she declined both of them, on the grounds that 'they wouldn't help'. Remember that immovable object I told you about earlier? Well, I had one right in front of me. I was pushing and pushing, but she just wouldn't budge. The only thing left was for her to get on with it and for me to deal with it.

That was until about Week 12 – the breakthrough.

On one fateful Tuesday, this client had come into the gym. She was pissed off and stressed about her brand-new iPhone that she'd mistakenly dropped in a puddle and now wasn't working. Luckily for her I had a 'friend' who was a little let's say 'dodgy', and could unlock stolen phones, and fix water-damaged phones … pretty much anything to do with tech; he was your guy. So, I told the client that if she gave me her phone, she'd have it back within a day or two and she wouldn't have to buy a new one. She was delighted and passed the phone over to me.

An hour later, I gave the phone to my 'friend' and he did his thing. He had it back to me a week later good as new. It took a little longer than expected, so the client had started using her husband's phone. On this fateful day, she called me from her husband's number to retrieve something off her mobile that was now back in my possession.

Are you ready?

She tells me I need to go into the photo section of the

iPhone and send a few photos of a certificate that she needed.

Instead, I bloody deleted one of them by mistake! So, I went to retrieve the photo from the deleted folder.

So, off I went to her deleted photos.

I wish I hadn't.

There it was … staring at me right in the face. Human flesh, naked skin, and the assortment of bodily crevices, just stand out from other pictures on a camera roll. I was immediately drawn to the slightly strange fleshy tones mixed with hints of red and purple. Then I look further and opened up the photo to make it larger and …

WHAM.

The most compromising sight greeted me. One which burnt a hole in my retinas. An image that has stayed with me ever since. It looked worse than L's bee-mauled manhood. It looked like an inflamed turkey neck.

'What on earth am I looking at here?' I asked myself as I'm turning the iPhone to look at it from different angles. I scrolled up, down. Are there anymore? Looking intently, like a leopard about to pounce on its prey, I saw a similar looking blurry colour palette, with three digits at the bottom right-hand side of the picture, signalling that it's a video.

My heart rate shot up two-fold. I was watching something I undoubtedly shouldn't have, but the voyeur in me couldn't put it down. I was fascinated but anxious at the same time.

All became clear. Here she was, our lovely Grand Canyon cowgirl videoing her backside.

You've just figured out why this chapter's called Bunch of Grapes, haven't you?

Ha!

What I saw here, dear readers, was a classic case of self-diagnosis. The diagnosis of the anal speed bump highway, the royal rectal raisins. Haemorrhoids, that looked like a set of anal wind chimes. Halle-fucking-lujah. It was now perfectly clear as to why the squat pattern was so painful. How could I not have guessed this? The poor client.

I put the phone down, and turned it off. I'd had enough.

How on earth was I going to broach this in our coming sessions? I'd never experienced this before, and for the life of me I didn't know how to approach it.

But I had to – for her health.

Before our next session, I spent hours trying to contemplate how I should deal with this. I should tell her. I definitely shouldn't. Yes. No. Yes. No. What will she think of me? I've got to be honest! No, keep your mouth shut. I had my own Gollum reflection moment, but he wasn't going to win.

I had to tell her. And I had to do it with as much sensitivity as I could muster. Her needs were far greater than mine.

When she arrived, I took her upstairs out of the gym and gave her back her phone, explaining that I saw something that answered why she was so uncomfortable in the squat position.

Her eyes opened, her cheeks blushed. She knew.

'Listen, seriously don't worry. Seriously. I've seen far worse than this,' I lied. I knew I needed to diffuse this situation quickly and make her feel at ease. There would be nothing worse than feeling those uncomfortable moments in between sets where she would hide her embarrassment in small talk. That was, if she didn't want to leave me as her trainer.

'It's cool. We've all been there,' I said, trying to ease the situation further. 'Try squatting double your bodyweight and this sort of thing becomes the norm.'

'Really? I feel so embarrassed,' she replied looking at the floor in shame.

'Honestly, it's perfectly normal, you know. I swear to you that probably more trainers than most have experienced this sort of thing. I wouldn't give any more thought on the matter. Upper body day today?' I asked, diverting the conversation to the present.

My strategy seemed to have worked. The heavy weight on the poor woman's shoulders lifted and her posture seemed relieved that the moment had passed. All those weeks of agonising over this trivial issue, knowing what the real reason as to why she couldn't push 100 per cent in her sessions, had now come to a close. We were in sync. We knew the secret, it was our secret, and we pushed on.

Now, credit where credit is due, she carried on like it was nothing and she trained harder than she normally did whilst still avoiding the squat and sitting down. To my surprise she didn't leave me, she stayed for the duration of her programme and she did that canyon trek in a great time. Nothing was ever mentioned of her issue thereafter, other than the silent knowledge that squats were hard to perform for the reasons now known to me. In this instance she knew best, and she knew that squatting wasn't for those with asteroids dangling on their backside.

I haven't seen her in years, and it's been a while since we spoke but a small word to the character in this chapter if you do read this, and you recognise yourself, then I want you to know that you did really well. I'm super proud of you. You trained hard and you achieved the results you deserved.

And thank you for not being a pain in the arse when I told you I'd seen yours.

SOVIET ARM WRESTLING

T he beautiful thing about living in a cosmopolitan city such as London is that you never stop experiencing different cultures or meeting new people. Whilst the far right may argue that multiculturalism has failed, there are those, like me, who embrace it in our work as a positive. Over my twenty-year stretch, I've had the pleasure of working alongside a multitude of different nationalities, with each one bringing their own spirit and ethos to the table. I've been fortunate enough to train clients who have come far and wide, including Kuala Lumpur, Siberia, Marrakesh, Tel Aviv, Kuwait, and Vilnius, to name just a few.

What strikes me more than anything, though, is the similarities I find in their mind-set with regards to business. Most of these clients are alpha male types, power hungry, controlling, domineering and aggressive. They take their work seriously and that is embedded into their health regime, hobbies and their finances.

For instance, one year I had a Japanese client who would work to the exact minute for everything he did. He would plan out his day so meticulously that there was no room for delay or patience. Our sessions were run on such militant time-keeping that it became too exhausting and he barely had any energy left to train. If I were one minute late, he would let me know, because he on the other hand would be there on time, every time. He was immaculate in every way. His super soft towel was always freshly laundered and folded to precise dimensions. He knew every part of our workout routine, from the time we took on each apparatus, down to how many seconds each muscle should be stretched for – God forbid we spent thirty seconds longer on one machine than another because that would throw his whole day out of kilter. Either way, it kept me on my toes, which was a good thing.

While this is an extreme example, other big business players weren't that dissimilar. OK, they weren't timing their days to the minute, but they would show characteristics of that mentality somewhere else in their lives. Each and every one of those business big weights all had an idea of what it was they wanted but soon came to learn that it was either unrealistic, or there was a better plan of action that I'd take them through.

And then there were the Russians.

Oh boy, the Russians.

As I have previously mentioned, I trained a lot of the big hitters from the Soviet bloc who were now living in London spending their money freely and actively looking after their health more. At the time of the final edit on this book, most of my ex-clients have now left the country, been sanctioned, or gone on the missing list. But what all of them had, when they were here, were the fantastical pre-conceived ideas that I'm about to talk about, but it was more how they interacted with each other that was absolutely fascinating to observe.

Whilst I was at The Cave, I ended up training a lovely Russian man who was a thoroughly nice, very smart, good looking and a normal guy given his acquaintances. There were times when he would want to do business while we trained, so more often than not I'd train him at his home instead of the gym, while he took breaks to make and receive calls. Nothing out of the ordinary – which was fine by me – home visits were always charged 1.5 times the normal rate. While this isn't uncommon, a lot of clients preferred training at The Cave, because it took them out of their comfort zone, and allowed them an hour of freedom from unwanted distractions. However, it always amazed me when any of these Russians wanted to leave their houses, considering how ridiculously amazing they were.

Situated in a quiet street in the suburbs of Hampstead sat a luxurious cream brick development, that rose out of the surrounding forestry like an ode to Hephaestus, the God of design. Green tinted windows reflected the hints of the summer light, where the walls elevated above the treetops, showing that man-made structures could sit with ease alongside nature. Square balustrades and cantilevered balconies surrounded the development hosting private swimming pools in each of the apartments. Built over 5,000 square feet, each resident's flat had its own concierge, private laundry service, every mod-con you could think of, and a pretty amazing car lift that when driven over a segment of the driveway, would lower itself into the ground like an elevator from a James Bond film. As you can imagine, this car park was a window for the wealth that resided in the apartments above. Spykers, Lamborghinis, rare vintage Aston Martins and over-customised Range Rovers, each of them freshly waxed and cleaned, glistened under the flush golden low lights situated in the ceilings.

The journey up from the car park to each flat was no different. The lift was stylishly adorned with gold trimmings, and the most beautiful buttons I've seen in any flat or hotel I've ever stayed in. It was an engineering masterpiece that wouldn't look out of place in the interior of a Bugatti. Each floor had two apartments that sat at each end of the hallway. Plush dark velvet flooring guided you to the front door where you would be greeted by a luxurious oak wood front door with a small spy hole and a glorious gold knocker that bore the Jewish Mezuzah (a small piece of parchment inscribed with parts of the Torah) that was also in burnished gold.

Whereas the architects had chosen the outside of the development, it was then up to each resident to decorate their home how they saw fit. I never got to see any of the other apartments in this building, but upon entering this particular flat, it was nothing short of, well, Russian.

What do I mean by that? Well, imagine taking yourself to an opulent eighteenth-century stately home whilst covering yourself in a jewelled shawl. Then put on some diamond encrusted gold boots, not forgetting the satin white diamante gloves (*because you can't touch anything*) and then wade through thick velour rugs that probably cost more than your house. Then you're getting somewhere.

Russians can be gaudy. That's fair, no? However, there is a reason for it, which actually lends to the subject, and the character of this chapter.

Without taking you into a detailed history of the fall of the Soviet bloc in the Nineties and why this fallout gave birth to some of the richest people on the planet, it's worth noting that, after the Second World War, the Soviet Union was in a period of transition. Historically a lot of the rich Russians today have come from very humble backgrounds. So when the change-over of presidents (and ideologies) came about, it was a minefield for those with the right connections and aptitude for making a lot of money. Never has there been a time in history when we are seeing the culmination of this wealth exposed on a global scale. Why does this then have a reflection on the way they act and show their money, you might ask?

Surprisingly, in a country whose ideology is 'the economy drives everything', it has led to a distinct amount of materialism running through the veins of the common man. Combine that with the want and the desire to be like the rest of the Western middle classes and you've got a hotbed for a show-off attitude. If we dig even deeper still, it is very apparent to this day that the hierarchy that exists in Russia is ruled from the top like it always has been. As George Orwell so eloquently wrote about the ethos of communism in *Animal Farm*: 'All animals are equal, but some animals are more equal than others.' It cannot be denied that the social pyramid in Russia is based on power. Money is power, strength is power. If you have money, you're going to show it, if you have strength, you're going to show it.

It's important to understand where this culture has come from in order to try and understand how the people operate in day-to-day life. I am sure that you have seen them on the street, or sat in a Lambo at the lights, and wondered how they came to be so blindingly wealthy. And this is where this story really kicks off …

The Russian in question had come to a slightly odd conclusion that he now wanted to train his arms more regularly. Nothing wrong with that, most guys want bigger arms. However, and there is a massive however, he was only interested in training one arm in particular. Why might you ask?

Well, I asked that very same thing, and it turned out that some brother of an uncle's daughter who married some step-sister's wife who had previously married his father's friend was a regional champion arm wrestler, and he was deemed to be the embodiment of a Greek god. Never mind that he lived in some mountain village where they drank vodka by the gallon, and wrestled bears for fun, what he did as a profession was macho, and that's all that mattered. It stood for elitism, and it made him the best man. Why that mattered to my client, I do not know, but I'd find out months later.

If he wanted to look like a fiddler crab, then so be it. 'Operation Popeye' was about to commence. And so, over the coming weeks, which turned into months, we carried on our existing training plan with the introduction on more emphasis on the shoulders, biceps and forearms. For the majority of people, building muscle is a very slow process, made easier by little to no stress, perfect nutrition and lots of sleep. Contrast that with a massive vodka-sinking, cigar-puffing, workaholic Russian and you get slow results. Really slow.

It was around month three of turning our lovely Ruski friend into Thanos that it all became evident as to why this odd process was underway. It was a mid-week summer's evening, when I had visited his house after his kids had returned from school.

'Matt, I vant you to meet someone. You'll love zis guy,' he

says with a big smile on his face.

As I entered his opulent long hallway, a small stocky, crew-cut shaven, olive-skinned man introduced himself by putting out his goliath sized hands and squeezing my own, to the point where I swear I heard metacarpals crunch under the weight.

'Nice to meet you, Matt, I'm Mikhail, I have heard many good zings about you,' he told me in his thick Russian accent. 'After you finish with him, you come see me,' he said pointing his Shrekesque finger into my chest. If I wasn't in good company, I'd think this guy was about to read me my last rites and have me executed.

As I moved through to the Russian's personal studio space, I couldn't help but notice the cacophony of noise coming from the living area that was in the adjacent room. There must have been at least twenty people arguing. My heart rate rose a little, which obviously showed itself on my face.

'Don't vorry, I'll show you after,' my client said, reassuring me with a small nod that nothing was wrong.

The thing about these alpha male Russians is that you can never quite tell where you stand with them. All those stories about war-torn Russians, Mafia contract killings and dodgy money laundering clichés spring to mind when you have a load of them in front of you shouting and hollering. There was an air of invincibility about him, and his unfailing optimism that I could turn his T-rex arms into something to behold was somewhat reassuring. I never felt like I was in trouble.

That was, of course, until after the session had ended, and he finished up by taking me through to the lounge area where all the noise was coming from.

'Gentlemen, zis is ze big guy, zis is … Matt,' he announced, a huge smile beaming on his face.

Now, picture this. The lounge was almost a perfect square, where a three-sided blood red sofa dominated the room. A huge mahogany coffee table the size of a super kingsize mattress sat in the middle hosting huge gold bowls of strawberries. There was no sign of empty vodka bottles, but instead sat a large humidor that had been left open protecting long lines of Cohiba and

Montecristo cigars. What surrounded this table, beneath the plume of thick sweet smelling cigar smoke, were four men all dressed in dark black attire, one of whom was Mikhail, the guy I had met earlier.

One by one, each of them stood to come and shake my hand and firmly gripped my shoulders. Looking back at each other they protested, shouting in their home dialect, like they were weighing me up to see which body part could fit inside their black brief cases that they had at hand. Once all the introductions were made, I was sat down next to my client in one of the corners of the oversized sofa, surrounded by the four men who puffed on their cigars and spoke in their mother tongue.

'Now to business gentlemen,' my client said to his colleagues.

This was obviously a sign to bring the noise levels up a notch as they all started furiously arguing with each other over something I couldn't understand. Legs and arms were flailing around; people were jumping up and down animating some physical beating of some kind. A lot of *'nyet'* and *'da'* were being yelled, which resembled a sort of old Palaeolithic era fire gathering.

Mikhail took out his phone and started shouting at my client, before turning to me to watch something on the small screen. It transpired that it was the hillbilly Russian I mentioned earlier, who was the regional arm-wrestling champion.

Forgive me, but arm wrestling is not exactly an entertaining sport, unless someone's arm gets ripped off, or we see one of those bloopers where the arm snaps in two. Normally it's over within seconds and it's a fairly static strength sport. That said, true arm wrestling is as much skill and technique as it is strength.

No matter what I did, they were adamant I was going to watch the video. I think I turned away once to look at my client and I was grabbed by Mr Goliath Hands by the face and forced to turn back to watch the video. And then it erupted. The living room area was being turned into a full-on competition. The sofa was being adjusted so that two Russians could go head-to-head on the coffee table. Leather jackets were being thrown off, and tshirts were being torn off in wild abandon. What I was about to witness was one of the strangest business meetings I'd ever attend. It was arm wrestling time, and *everyone* had to compete.

In this moment, it became clear as to why my client wanted to look like Rafa Nadal's forearm on steroids. To beat these other guys in the room. That's it.

The challenge then came my way. My client wanted to face off against his own trainer.

Needless to say, I didn't feel like sleeping six-foot under the house that night so after a brief face off, I let the arm go and gave the win to my client. It was then the turn of each of my client's colleagues. However, this time I was holding it down for all the other PTs out there. I got the feeling it was worse being thought of as a weakling than it would have been to be sent to a Russian gulag, so I wasn't backing down. I held my own and I brought down three out of the four. I got respect. I'd like to say that my client won all of his wrestles. However, that'd be lying. He got demolished. Back to the drawing board, I thought.

As the testosterone died down, and everyone put their tops back on, I caught the client's wife in the corner of my eye, who had entered the room with more strawberries. I used this as my excuse to leave the mixture of smoke and sweat and get up to ask her what the hell is going on. She told me that that's the way they do business, which I guess harks back to their long and dark history. If you ever wanted to see a true dick-swinging contest, then go be a guest during a Russian business meeting. It's not for the faint hearted, so make sure you've got strong enough arm strength to at least beat one of them, otherwise, much like the bowls of strawberries, you'll end up on the dessert menu.

A big bowl of Rice Putin.

PISS POOR PERFORMANCE

A s you're probably beginning to realise, my PT career is defined by surreal and somewhat sketchy moments. For many years, I always assumed that I simply attracted the freaks and weirdos, the eclectic, the highly unusual and the unpleasant. Hell, even at university I was known as the 'Pikey Magnet'. I'd always had a skill for catching burglars in the act, or see flashers, or witness muggings and see fights brewing long before they'd happen in bars and nightclubs. You could say that I have an unusual third eye for the strange and deranged, but this next story I'm going to tell you about gives me the comfort to know that there are other trainers out there who have just as interesting clients as I do.

It's 2014, the year of the surreal. A dog surfed at the sixth annual surf city contest at Huntington Beach, *Sharknado* got a sequel, Dutch artist Bart Jansen turned his dead cat into a remote-controlled helicopter, and Malaysian airlines flight 370 disappeared into nowhere … and then Courtney Love claimed to have found it on Google Maps.

You could say fucked up things like this happen every year, but 2014, and the client I'm about to tell you of, sticks in my mind as one of the weirdest things I've ever witnessed.

The Three Amigos were now complete with Irish recently joining me and Danger. Kane too. We were all working at the grotty basement gym The Cave, which was now falling into more disrepair, but still attracting the rich and the famous. Paint peeled from the walls and dank mould had started growing up through the bathroom floor giving off a reeking musty smell which told you immediately that the place had multiple damp issues. The basement sat below a low-key café whose fridges and freezers would regularly leak through the floorboards at night, so that each morning we'd have to wade through last night's defrosted chicken juice. Combine this with overflowing toilets and you've got yourself a workout area that people work hard at wanting to leave. Even though we weren't employed by the owner, the gym would miraculously become our responsibility whenever any cleaning would need to be done. So, every morning you'd have my good self, a hung-over Irishman, and the head of the baby mafia – Danger – all scrubbing the floors and cleaning the bathrooms. By the time the first client came through the doors, it was cleaner than a priest on a Sunday. This was repeated every day, five days a week, for the remaining six months all of us worked in this cesspit.

Despite the inadequacies of this gym, we made it work with endless banter and good vibes. For some reason the smell never put any clients off, and we managed to pull in a tidy sum. The reason we achieved this was down to the simple fact that we all knew the value of the facility to the client. I can't stress how important it is to have the utmost respect for where you work. I have seen too many PTs treat their facilities with disregard, not realising that the client puts great significance on the gym that they will be training in. All of us should see our place of work as our own and treat it as such.

However, to say that the client has as much respect as we do is a different story altogether, which will be illustrated in this vignette. When you share facilities with other trainers, you learn their training habits, how they conduct themselves and you always see the same faces at the same times of the day. There was one client in particular, who happened to be trained by one of the other trainers in the gym at the time. And this female client had all four of us stumped.

As I've alluded to Danger's lustful capacity for the XX chromosome in a previous chapter, he was very outwardly thinking about our colleague's client. A small woman in her early forties, with breasts like two pert melons hidden by the smallest Lulu Lemon nipple holsters you could ever witness. With shades of Sienna Miller to her, she was a beautiful woman, with a whiff of the Bohemian. Anyone remotely attractive was like catnip to Danger (even though she was there to get in shape for her upcoming wedding) and he had no qualms in expressing his deepest love for her after every session.

'Cor, I'd eat chips out of her knickers' was a well-known phrase he'd often use when a client had left.

But, what was to happen with this client left even Danger realising that women can be just as filthy as men.

It was a morning after a very busy evening in the café, when the leaks in the ceiling had emptied their putrid load onto our gym floor to greet us at the break of dawn. That very same evening there was a torrential downpour of rain which gushed down the outside walls from the overflowing gutters. In times like these it called for the central heating to be ramped up to breaking point, and a certain amount of due diligence in knowing where the leaks were and where to strategically place buckets across the gym floor. To us this was normal, but to an outsider it must have physically felt like a poor-man's Bikram yoga studio. It was hot, it was wet, and it stank.

I arrived around mid-morning. Irish was in the office sleeping off a case of self-induced Captain Morg-Man-flu, Danger was stretching his first victim of the day, and our bohemian bride-to-be had just walked in. Nothing unusual, yet.

The gym was built in two parts. One area hosted dark metal rigs that supported the barbells and weights, whilst the larger area was used for boxing, aerobic activities and stretching. It was a fairly small space set out over a long oblong shape with toilets and changing areas built into the sides, but it accommodated us well.

Halfway through the session, the Bride-To-Be moved into the main area of the gym.

'I'm bored of this session now, let's do something fun,' she said impassively.

Her trainer who I'll call, for the sake of this chapter, Mr Unfortunate, pulled a skipping rope off one of the racks.

What happened next was a face-off between the client and her trainer. Bear in mind the gym is small, so we could all hear what everyone was saying.

'I haven't skipped since I was a child. I don't really think I can do it. Oh god,' she said sheepishly, as he passed her the rope.

'It's OK, let me demonstrate,' Mr Unfortunate replied, hoping that he could bring the client round.

She tried, she failed. Skipping is one of those things that if you haven't practiced for a while, it can be incredibly frustrating to find your feet again.

'I can't do it,' she said stamping on the ground. 'I read that skipping was bad for women anyway. It says it puts too much pressure on your pelvis. I can't get injured before the wedding,' she continued.

Here we go, I thought. Another battle against this month's nonsensical *Cosmopolitan* article.

'Well, you wanted to do something different,' Mr Unfortunate stated. However, to our colleague's credit, patience was one of his strong points and he persevered for a solid ten minutes, showing her how to flick the rope, what type of jump she should do and why it wasn't dangerous for a female pelvis.

And to her credit, B-T-B got it. Not only did she get it, but she was also pretty good at it, and boy was she pleased with herself. The smile said it all.

And this is where it goes a little bit awry.

I noticed Danger wandering around the trainer, his eyes fixed on the client's feet, hand to his jaw like the statue of Rodin's Thinker.

'Mate, mate, your client is skipping in a puddle,' Danger

whispered to the trainer.

He didn't take too much notice, allowing his client to finish her set. Danger came over to me, looked me straight in the eye and said:

'Boods, does that puddle look … a bit odd … to you?' Pointing with a quick head flick toward the skipping client. I can't quite see any puddle if I'm honest, just a bit of water being splashed up over her ankles. I'm guessing it could be last night's storm residue.

'Nah, mate, what you on about? It's The Cave, it's always like that here,' I said, trying to make sense of it all.

'Nah nah nah, take another look. Look slightly higher up,' he said eyes as wide as the moon with a deadpan look on his face.

I squinted harder to see what he was talking about, and then I caught on. Danger looked back at me with the look of the devil in his eye. We both clocked what had happened.

By now, Irish's FOMO had kicked in and joined the discussion. Danger alerted him to what he was talking about, and in true Irish fashion, he said what we were all thinking.

'What in the Jaysus, horse?' he bellowed. Never the one for subtlety is Irish. 'You better do something bout dat, horse,' he carried on pointing at the client.

Our colleague seemed nonplussed. He might be patient, but he wasn't the sharpest tool in the box.

B-T-B looked over at us three, slightly out of breath, and jumped up and down before simply proclaiming, 'Oh, don't worry fellas, I just had a pee.'

Danger looked at me. Irish looked at Danger. I looked at Irish. Mr Unfortunate looked at all three of us red-faced. He didn't know how to react, or what to do:

'Oh, oh, what? Oh, ummm, I thought that was a puddle from the ceiling,' he said shakily.

'No, love, just me having a wee,' as she carried on skipping, with a smile on her face. She was skipping quite happily, knowingly, in a large puddle of her own piss.

So, I want to stop us here and ask what would you do in this situation?

Bear in mind this is not your client, or your studio. A woman is not only pissing herself but then happily jumping up and down in it, causing a melee of orange Fanta like liquid all over the mats and the kettle bells … and she's not looking like she's stopping any time soon. Quite the opposite, in fact, she's finding it thoroughly amusing that four male trainers were watching her micturate on the floor.

So, what do you do?

Irish looked like he was about to bring back Captain Morgan from his far-off travels, Danger had gone strangely coy, probably battling his inner instinct to find any female excretion mildly arousing, whilst I was trying to find a pneumatic drill so I could dig my way out of The Cave. Instead, I made for the office and hid myself in there. Mr Unfortunate on the other hand was left to sort out the situation.

Except, that's exactly what he didn't do.

No, in fact, he was left completely embarrassed and flummoxed for the rest of the session, while the lovely pool of yellow liquid lay shimmering off the studio's white lights. It also didn't help that the gym was hotter than the sun, and the smell began emanating through to the office. Irish had now turned a whiter shade of pale and left for the upstairs toilet. Danger had come to his senses and was now curled up on the floor in the foetal position laughing hysterically, and I was rummaging through the office cupboards trying to find disinfectant and white latex gloves.

But the real joke was that she didn't even offer to clean it up, or even remotely show any remorse, or awkwardness. It wasn't even like she'd recently given birth (a genuine issue of pelvic floor instability) that she could blame it on. It was literally left to our poor defeated colleague to clean up the piss. And we never found out why she just decided to piss her pants.

However, out of the blue in January 2018, I received this enquiry through my website:

On 7 Jan 2018, at 6:16pm, xxx@gmail.com   wrote:

Hi there! I am very interested in hiring a personal trainer. I am based in St Johns Wood and would love to train with you! My focus is on getting back in shape after my wedding in 2014. I've let myself go a bit so I'm looking for a motivating personal trainer to get me back to where I used to be.

My reply:

On 7 Jan 2018, at 7:23pm, Matt Hodges math@themphmethod.com wrote:

Dear xxx,

Thank you for your enquiry into personal training with The MPH Method. Forgive me for saying, but I think we may know each other. Did you used to train with **XXX** at **XXX**? I used to be a PT there back at this time and your name really rings a bell. If this is correct then you might remember I was the only trainer who wore branded uniform?
If not, ignore me, I am more than happy to help you with your goals. Is there a   convenient time and number I can ring you on to discuss further?

Her reply:

On 8 Jan 2018, at 10:42pm, xxx@gmail.com wrote:

Oh my gosh! Yes. How embarrassing. Are you still there? Does **XXX** still work there? Oh my life, I remember the last time I went there. Cringe! I'm so sorry please ignore this enquiry.

There are moments in life when you ponder on how the world can work in mysterious ways and this was definitely one of them. I just wished I had the balls to ask her *why* she took the piss.

After our emails, it was me however, who ended up pissing myself laughing.

PART THREE

THE OVER SELLERS, THE TAKERS AND THE OPPORTUNISTS

LESSON THREE:

Don't shag your clients, don't try to shag your clients, don't even think about shagging your clients.

The thing I find the hardest about being a PT, and not unlike many other trainers, is keeping a consistent income. The fitness industry is over-subscribed and competition is rife. Main chain gyms incentivise their PTs by pushing non-realistic targets, that either drive them into the dirt or make them leave with the clients. Smaller, boutique outfits that have a business model built on PTs renting their space will also fall foul of trainers upping and leaving when a cheaper option arrives. The thing is, being a freelance personal trainer isn't like working for a large organisation or company; you can't just pick and choose the contracts you want. It's an endless treadmill of pressure to secure new clients and retain them. That pressure alone, in my opinion, is why the industry is full of charlatans who oversell, devise get rich quick schemes, or promise you'll have Angelina's butt or Brad Pitt's abs 'in just six weeks'. It's because no-one can sustain this shit for too long.

Anyone who sells you a 'Buy my 10 week program that can make you lose 50 pounds!' program won't reveal the secret that you're only going to drink one spinach smoothie a day and do all untold damage to your body, but who gives a fuck about health when you can lose that much weight, right?

You get my point.

In an industry as fickle as health and fitness, it's no surprise to me that a lot of PTs get stuck into the lower level moral underground. Multi-level marketing (MLM) schemes and the idea of the quick buck are systematically fed to us by the industry itself. I mean, how many times have you seen someone trying to sell a six-figure fitness salary on social media as if it's as easy as 1-2-3? If those people were truly making six figures, they probably wouldn't be telling you how they did it – they'd be on a beach somewhere. I give you my sincere apology if you're one of those and are offended by my 'bitchcraft – the art of pissing people off by telling them the truth – but it's the truth and we all know it.

Case in point…

I knew a guy who lived with his wealthy parents. He didn't have a job but drove his parents' cars around his private estate, made a few short movies about his 'luxury' lifestyle, wrote an e-book on how to get rich quick, and, I shit you not, a few months later he was charging £10,000 for an hour's seminar!

And you know what the most unbelievable thing was?

People paid it.

So, who do we hate? The player or the game? The individual or the industry? We seem to have found ourselves in a self-perpetuating mess, where success means selling your soul just to survive. The world now operates through lenses of social media, meaning it's easier to sell your trade, as dubious and devious as it may well be, globally.

Even with apps and discounts and more PTs than ever before, personal training is still deemed a luxury. Those that can afford it are often in a better financial position than the trainer themselves. And herein lies a serious psychological issue. PTs constantly see, hear and feel what life is like where the grass is greener. This makes you hungry. Hungry for material success. Hungry for what your clients have. So, when opportunities arise, or the allure of making easy money, you find yourself taking them.

When I first qualified, I did it on the basis that I already had a client base, so I needed the qualification to justify the insurance. Was it the wrong reason to get into the industry? Maybe. However, what was instilled in me from my parents was a level of professionalism and pride in everything I did. If I were going to be an architect, I'd go to every meeting in a suit and produce the best work I could. If I were going to be a builder, I'd be on time, every time, and fulfil the job to the client's specifications. If I were going to be a PT, I wanted to give the client what they were paying for and that meant not spending the hour talking about myself, talking to my colleagues, or – even worse – on the phone! This is not rocket science, be proud of everything you do and you will be a success story (you don't need to buy an e-book on how to earn a six-figure salary!). Sure, I've had my fair share of things that tempted me. I've been offered a brand new Audemars Piguet Offshore watch for sex – worth 40 grand! The watch, not the sex. I've been offered a Lamborghini for a week. I've been told by a male client that they were secretly in love with me and that we should escape to the French Riviera to get married (this happened twice, actually). I've had clients, male and female, drop their drawers before a massage hoping I'd give them a happy ending, and I've also been offered a significant amount of investment for a new studio in exchange to do something I knew was highly illegal.

All of which I turned down … well, apart from the Lambo which you'll read about later.

Whilst some of you may be saying what the hell was I thinking, and believe me I was verbally berated for years by Danger, Kane and Irish for not taking the watch, professionalism was always at the core of what I did. While others around me have a moral compass that was permanently set to the ends of their bell-ends, or had about as much professionalism as Harvey Weinstein at an audition, I always had boundaries that I never crossed.

What follows in this chapter are three examples of the oversellers, the taker and the opportunists who sit on both sides of that fence: The trainer and the client.

JONNIE

Cast your mind back to when you were at school and think about the kids who you used to know. You had the jocks, the emos, the goths and the geeks, the inbetweeners, the teachers' pets, the grubby kids who always smelt, the kids who always had stringy bogeys hanging out their noses, and the kids who always came last on sports day. Now relate that back into your own friendship groups, and in almost every situation you'd find there was the leader of the group, the alpha male/female and then there was always the one who was the butt of everyone's jokes – the class clown. If you don't know if that was you or not, it was you. Sorry to be the one to tell you.

In the dying light of 2014, the Three Amigos had our very own class clown – Jonnie.

Jonnie was a medium height, wavy-haired, spotty faced smooth talking Australian charmer who hailed from a farmland area called Dubbo, New South Wales. He had come to the UK to do a few years in PT, and to travel the country with a few of his Bogan backyard mates. After we'd all left The Cave, we ended up all working together in a fairly small private exclusive studio, so we had to get on. Whilst everyone has the right to be stupid, there are some, like Jonnie, who abused their privilege, and soon became an irritant to most of the PTs who worked there. Not a bad guy by any stretch, but he just rubbed everyone up the wrong way with his laziness and his attitude towards his clients.

During Jonnie's tenure at this establishment, he would go on to commit some serious faux pas with regards to professionalism that still, to this day, no one else could get away with. Never mind the audacity of Kane faking Tourette's, Jonnie would produce some absolute whoppers that left destruction in his wake, yet somehow left him unscathed. For instance:

One morning, one of the receptionists found Jonnie curled up asleep on one of the physio tables. It turned out that he had been using the gym as a home for a few nights, after being evicted from his flat and had nowhere to stay.

Jonnie doing what Jonnie did best then managed to convince one of his clients to house him in one of the properties that they owned. However, there were stipulations to this move. The proviso was that Jonnie would have to do the place up (which would be funded by the client) in return for free rent. Not unlike the problem with PTs I've mentioned before, apparently Jonnie had now turned into a painter and decorator, electrician and plumber overnight. I would hazard to say that the extent of his knowledge didn't go farther than turning a tap on and off.

Well, as you can imagine, it didn't last long before the client realised that Jonnie was just a PT and was in no way anything resembling a builder.

It turned out that she had given Jonnie nearly ten grand to do up the flat, which he had spunked somewhere along the line (there was no evidence of any work actually being done). It seemed like finally, the game was up for this kid and he had to be told in no uncertain terms that he needed to pay back the money or else (the 'or else' was unspecified but was clearly not an idle threat). And yet, despite expecting to find him six feet under or in the river with bricks attached to his feet (there was no way he could repay the money) he appeared back in the gym, unscathed and unaffected. Another client who was left all the worse for training with Jonnie.

If a client losing ten grand wasn't enough to prove that Jonnie was the walking talking version of an overseller, a taker AND an opportunist, then what came next would prove to us all that there was no limit to ol' Mick Dundee's lovechild's skulduggery.

It was about six months into us all working together when we realised the non-existent boundaries that Jonnie crossed as we started noticing that he'd often go into one of the therapy rooms with one of his clients, I'll call her 'Karma' for the sake of this chapter. It didn't take Sherlock Holmes to figure out what was going on when both parties left the room red faced and sweaty. This obviously got Danger's back up as there was someone else in the vicinity getting more female attention than him.

'Jonnie, bruv, the only thing you're going to give that client in that room is a 'boregasm'. May as well stop now,' Danger said half-mocking.

We all knew what they were doing, but what we didn't know was that the client was actually married with two young children.

'Shuddup, mate, stop havin' a whinge would ya, you've just got tall poppy syndrome,' Jonnie replied in his thick Australian accent.

This whole saga with Karma went on for a good few months, where the majority of their sessions were spent in the therapy room. The rest of us were upstairs frantically ordering antiseptic hand wash knowing the room would be like a scene from a honeymoon suite at a dive motel under a UV spotlight.

However, this didn't last much longer.

About four months into their physio couch 'relationship', I was sat at the reception desk with the two girls who manned the phones. Danger was on my right hand side looking at his diary claiming, 'There are too many men in my diary, I'm going to swap these around'. Irish, on the rare occasion, was training himself, and Jonnie was lurking by the front door awaiting his Karma.

Then in she came – and off they went to the now bored indifference of the four of us at reception. However, about fifteen minutes later, the front door of the studio banged loudly and in came a short, balding, irate and stocky gentleman in his fifties, clearly out of breath.

'Where's Karma, I just saw her come in here,' the man barked at the receptionist.

'Excuse me, sir, who are you?' she replied politely.

'I'm her fucking husband. WHERE IS SHE?' he shouted.

At this point, the other receptionist baled and Danger stood up, while I did my best to stare-down this fella.

'I'm sorry, sir,' the receptionist replied. 'She's with her trainer.'

'I bet she is!' he yelled, looking around to see if he can see any doors to the rooms.

I noticed him eyeing up the office as he changed his stance and turned to make his advances towards it.

Danger quickly moved into action, standing eye to eye with the man. 'You ain't going in there, fella, that's our private office,' Danger says to the husband sternly.

During this stand-off, I quickly bolted down the stairs to the therapy room area. I could still hear the furore upstairs so I took the opportunity to quickly knock on the door. Nothing, not a peep. I put my ear to the door, but strangely heard nothing. I knocked again. Still nothing. OK, sod this, I thought. I flung open the door and…

The two of them were just sat there hugging in some weird statuesque embrace. Both eyes closed, not moving. It was like two praying mantises in a tantric exchange, except Jonnie was naked. Karma, however, was fully clothed.

'Alright you two, time to get moving,' I said trying not to look anyone in the eye. 'Your fucking husband has just barged in.'

The news clearly sunk in as both them frantically gathered their things as if the building was on fire.

'Oh, fuck!' Jonnie muttered. 'Matty, go keep him occupied will ya, mate?'

I was now half expecting the husband to come bombarding down the stairs, but to my surprise Danger had him sat down at reception with a coffee, waiting patiently. I came up and took a look at both of them wondering how Danger had calmed the man down. Both receptionists eyeballed me with a '?' look in their eyes, while Danger assertively had his hand on the husband's shoulder.

As the lovebirds arrive on the top deck, the husband jumps straight out of his seat and grabs his wife by the arm pulling her out the front door.

'You'll be hearing from the press about this,' he shouted back at us all, clearly directing his anger at Jonnie.

'Listen mate, I just want you to know that …' Jonnie started as the two paced off into the distance arguing with each other.

As we all watched them fight their way to their car, Jonnie looked at all of us and gave a large sigh of relief with a thick Aussie, 'Fuck me, I was packing darkies there, mayyyte'.

I was in a state of bemused shock. So, naturally, took the piss.

'Jonnie, why were *you* naked?' I giggled.

As usual, he saw the funny side, and within a day or two he had forgotten it had happened. However, once again the reality of the moral ineptitude of Jonnie had consequences for everyone else besides from him. We later learnt that Karma had got divorced following the debacle at the gym. While Jonnie probably wasn't the sole reason that they split up, he was definitely the architect in making it happen, though I'm not entirely sure he cared too much. And I wouldn't be surprised if it happened again. But, as Jonnie often said, 'You only live once mayyyte.'

So, if any of you PTs out there get any crazy ideas about following in Jonnie's footsteps, then all I have to say to you, in perfect Jonnieesque Bogan verse is – 'Don't be a dickhead, ya fackin' dickhead.'

THE USB DJ

This chapter is dedicated to Danger, and his outstanding ability to manipulate a situation for his own personal benefit, especially when it comes to women. The Artful Dodger of the fitness industry, Danger's unscrupulous tactics gave him a chance to pull off one of the most audacious acts I've ever seen from a person, let alone a PT.

It's 2015, when I'd recently invited a well-known socialite who had found me through one of the cast on *EastEnders* to rent out a spare room I had in my apartment in west London. I've never been a big one for the live-big lifestyle but this socialite, let's call her 'Chelsea', couldn't wait to move in.

Much to the disappointment of my long-term girlfriend who I will call 'The Great Dane', Chelsea had legs up to her ears, long blonde hair flowing down her back, and had a voice that could melt most Sloany pony-obsessed men. It's fair to say, Chelsea was a stunner. She was financially dependent on her father, but he didn't seem too fussed with her excessive lifestyle. But we, on the other hand, had to often accommodate her pretentious friends in my living room cutting up fat lines of cocaine on the coffee table, speaking fast and loudly explaining every two minutes how soft my beloved dog Honey's fur was.

That said, we rarely ever crossed paths during the day, with her coming home from a night out as I'd be leaving for work. Due to her transient lifestyle, she never set up a permanent residency in London. I should have probably seen this as a warning sign for what was to come, but I ignored it on the grounds that her rent was being paid by mummy and/or daddy.

Now, given that this little missy was a well-connected socialite, who do you think was ringing me up every Friday to see if he could come round? Danger, of course. The idea of an attractive, famous socialite (think Paris Hilton, Tamara Beckwith, et al) who could pay for her own drinks and drugs, was like a choirboy to a catholic priest for Danger – the Holy Grail.

And Danger couldn't believe I was living with her. He would question me till the cows came home about her lifestyle, whether she was single and if she wasn't single would she be averse to a little side hustle. With him. Eventually, it became too annoying to delay so I invited Danger round to the house in the hopes they would meet and she would tell him directly to fuck off. That backfired because soon enough Danger was always round mine. Then, even sooner, it felt like Danger was living at mine.

They got on well. Too well. She never succumbed to his charms, so he moved on to all and any of her friends. Which was even worse.

One day, out of the blue, I received a text saying she was giving notice on the flat, because she'd decided that she wanted to go on 'tour' around the Balearics, hosting exclusive parties for the run up to opening week in Ibiza. She told me that while she had all her ducks in order, she wanted to know if I had any 'media' contacts (i.e., clients) who could DJ and would be willing to go on tour with her. The Great Dane and Honey were delighted she was leaving home, of course. At the time, I didn't know anyone suitable, and I was just racking my brains as to how I was going to break the news to the man baby, Danger. He'd be devastated, he'd be bereft if she left. His conquest would be left unfinished, a Napoleon without his revolution, a Messi without his left foot, Hugh Hefner without his bunnies. What would he do with his time now? I had to break it to him slowly … on seconds thoughts, best to rip the band aid off.

'Mate, Chelsea's leaving. There's no point you coming round anymore. It's over,' I said to Danger on our first Monday back working together. I wasted zero time with zero fucks.

'What? Eh? What am I gonna do now?' he replied flustered, as if he had nothing more to live for.

'Well, unless you suddenly become a DJ overnight, there's not much hope for you, pal.'

Danger looked at me completely puzzled. He stared at the floor, thought about it for a second, and then looked back up at me again with a small smirk. I could hear the cogs turning,

'What sort of DJ is she looking for, mate?' he asked.

'Someone who can play music at her parties, a DJ, you know – turntables, decks, vinyls, tote bags, an inflated sense of self, etc,' I told him.

'Yeah, but you know, like what kind of DJ?' he fired back.

'I dunno, mate, she's looking for a proper DJ, someone who's probably got access to, I dunno, music.' I could see his brain whirring.

Danger looked at me, his hands out at his side like he was about to invite me in for a big hug.

'Mate, me. I CAN DJ!'

I knew it. I knew I should never have brought this up.

'Since when have you ever DJ'd?'

'What you on about, Boods, I can DJ. And it ain't that hard. This day and age it's all digital anyway. No need for Technics and amps and shit. Listen, I tell you what, let her know I'm game, and see what she says.'

There is no end to the lengths Danger will go to either get laid or earn a bit of extra cash.

'You've got her number, you let her know,' I said. 'You do realise you probably have to show that you can do this. I mean, it's not like you haven't been spending copious amounts of time at ours these past few months, and you've NEVER once mentioned you can DJ. You realise she'll know you're full of shit, right?' I asked, dumbfounded that he's even considering this as a possibility.

'Na, man you leave it to me,' he said with an unwavering level of confidence. 'I'll sort her right out, Boods, don't you worry.'

I wasn't worried at all. In fact, I was starting to like the humiliation he was going to suffer when she learned he could barely spell 'DJ' let alone become one.

Like any landlord/tenant agreement, Chelsea had to see out the final few weeks before she left for a sunnier climate. Things were steadily moving ahead and arrangements were being made for the first party she'd be hosting. The following four weeks went a little something like this:

Day 1 – Danger sends the text saying he can DJ. Socialite gets excited.

Day 3 – After a bit of haggling and Danger playing her a 'set.' Miss Socialite books Danger for two months, yes *two months* on the road. He gets paid £1000 per gig, and expenses.

Day 4 - Danger leaves our current gym four weeks early to 'brush up on his DJ'ing skills'. He also stops paying his rent on his flat.

Day 8 – I get a phone call at 9pm … 'Boods, can I borrow your Spotify account? I need some tracks.' He sounds worried. I give him access. The beauty about Spotify is you can see search history.

Day 11 – I call Danger after three days of letting him find some music. 'Mikey, you muppet why are you searching for Michael Jackson tracks? You do realise what kind of parties she throws right? It's progressive dance/house,' I tell him.

Day 12 - Spotify search history: 'Pro aggressive Dance and House' and 'Progressive Dance/House mixes'.

Day 13 – 'Boods, name a DJ will ya? A decent one. One that you know they'd like.'

Day 14 – Spotify search history:
  'Carl Cocks'
  'Carl Cocks playlist'
  'Carl Cox'
  'Carl Cox free playlist'

'Fuck Carl Cox'

'DJ playlist'

'Free DJ playlist'

Day 16 – Chelsea moves out. Leaves used condoms under her bed and her room in a mess. Doesn't think to reimburse me for the latex marigolds and bleach I now have to buy.

Day 18 – I get a phone call at 12.17am. 'Boods, this mixing lark is hard. I need a USB stick, have you got one?' He must be desperate … it's gone midnight, and he's thinking about USB sticks. I lend him one the next day.

Day 21 – USB stick isn't big enough. Danger buys another one. Tells me he's got a load of new tunes. I receive an email saying I've signed up for Spotify Premium.

Day 22 – I get a phone call mid-afternoon. 'Boods I've got my first set done. Wanna hear it?' It sounds remarkably professional. Maybe there won't be any humiliating cannon fodder for the banter factory after all. I cannot believe he actually might pull this off.

Day 24 – Latex marigolds do not suffice. I invoice Miss Socialite for a professional clean.

Day 26 – All is quiet on the West London Front.

Day 28 – Danger calls me to thank me for putting him in touch with Miss Socialite. They're about to board the plane. He does not reimburse me for the Spotify Premium account.

And then it all goes quiet. To the dismay of us all, Danger had left the gym to tour with my old housemate disguising himself as a DJ. I hadn't heard from him since he left, but it was about three weeks in to the tour when we all started getting the pictures of wild nights, neon signs, shirtless bodies and vibrant fluoro body paint. Danger's up on the faux decks with his wife beater vest, throwing shapes in front of the crowds, with pupils the size of satellite dishes. It seemed like it was going well.

That was until about week five, Day 63.

I arrived at the studio to open up for the first set of clients. Today was a busy day, and I knew I probably wouldn't see sunlight until at least four hours later when I had my first break. This gym in particular was a large 4,000 square foot room, situated in an old church, with a reception area that overlooked the gym through panes of transparent glass. To my surprise, whilst on client three, I notice the figure of a short stocky cheeky faced toddler that looked uncannily like Danger.

I manoeuvred myself around the client, and to my surprise it was the man himself at the reception desk, animatedly talking to the owner with a tan that wouldn't look out of place in a Benidorm time-share meeting. I excused myself from my client and wandered over to see my old friend.

'What are you doing back?' I asked, surprised to see him.

'Oh, mate, I had a nightmare didn't I? Couldn't keep up the DJ lark. Got found out. Didn't help that you cancelled your Spotify Premium account though, did it?' he said whispering.

'Wait wait, you mean to say, she kicked you out? You're back for good?'

Danger took me to one side, speaking to me in his 'Don't look at me whilst I'm talking about something secret' voice. 'Mate, she cottoned on. I kept playing the same playlist all the time, didn't I? I don't know how to mix. I don't know how to use these fancy digital decks they had. I just downloaded what I thought was a good DJ set and played that. On repeat.'

'So what happened? How did she find out?' I reply, holding back fits of laughter.

It transpired that on one of the nights he'd forgotten to update the USB stick with a new set. Unable to swiftly download some new tunes, and given that they were already at the venue, there was only one thing he could do – play directly from Spotify… but guess what? I'd disabled the Premium account, thinking he didn't need it.

So, for those of you that don't know the app – you can't just roll off a playlist in the free version, because adverts spring up between songs. Well, during the transition of LMFAO's *I'm Sexy And I Know It* came a pop-up advert that gave the game away! I'm told that it was an awkward evening, with Danger being taken back to the hotel and flying back home the next day, tail between his legs.

At this point we both started laughing at the sheer audacity of his strategy.

Not only had he lied about being a DJ, he'd managed to pull it off for a solid five weeks until he got found out. He hadn't paid any of his rent on his London flat, he hadn't paid for any of the tracks he was using (he was using illegal software to rip them) and he hadn't told the gym owner that he was leaving. And now, after all the fun and games, he was here trying to get his old job back and save his flat from the debt collectors. That's when I learned the lesson that there is no end to what an over seller, a taker or an opportunist will do.

Danger and I stayed in contact with Chelsea for a few years, and just like everything else in this messed up world of fitness, he ended up training her again on a random Bootcamp retreat in Greece. This time though … the music was provided.

Oh, how the turntables.

SNAKES IN THE GRASS

The increase of early morning starts was starting to give me grey hairs. I felt like I was nearing the end of yet another tenure with the current studio – the old church. I'd always had ideas of setting up on my own – it's every PT's dream to one day say a place is yours, a testament to the amount of hard work you've put in over the years. It was a natural progression for me to go from employed, to self-employed and then go it alone. And when a small commercial property became available down the road, after eight years of service, I was finally ready to have my own place that suited the exclusive clientele I was pulling in. It was my time. I handed in my notice, and my clients were notified of my departure. Part of my current contract stated that I could not solicit clients, so I made it perfectly clear as to where I was going, and I left it at that.

I had grand delusions of becoming the next big star in the fitness world. With my new private luxury space open in the heart of wealthy Hampstead, and a very expensive shiny new website, I thought every man and his dog would know I was there. By some miracle, without doing any marketing, no advertising, no shouting from the rooftops, my ego had got the better of me, and I thought I could run the business on my reputation alone. I naively thought clients would be magnetically pulled towards the studio's front door, just as it had at my previous studios.

How wrong I was.

And then came the slump. The harsh reality.

With commercial rents, business rates, equipment loans and leases to pay with only a handful of sessions coming through the door, I started to sweat. The bank balance was dwindling as quickly as the direct debits were increasing. Water, electricity and air conditioning were now something I had to think about. Insurance on contents, public liability, balance sheets and quarterly tax returns stared me in the face. I left the old church studio because of a few grey hairs. Now, I was staring at a silver fox in the mirror at the age of 33.

There are those moments as a struggling self-employed PT when you wish for just one new client to take that horrible burden of fear off your shoulders. It's almost like a bath being filled to the brim, knowing that it's going to overflow and ruin your home. So when, suddenly, an enquiry comes in, it's as if they pull the plug and all the water goes down the plughole, relieving that pressure and saving your home from a floody disaster.

However, this time it was from an ex-client of mine from the old church, who I really didn't want to hear from, called 'The Snitch'.

The Snitch was an entitled do-gooder who walked with an air of arrogance and who I'd wanted to leave behind because of the way she had acted. Social media now notoriously call these types of people 'Karen', which she fitted to a T. Bedazzled head to toe in diamonds, she'd be the first to complain to a manager if anything was wrong. If there wasn't enough toilet roll in the bathrooms or if the towels hadn't been folded properly, I knew about it. I'm sure she'd be doing the same everywhere she went. It seemed her sole purpose in life was to not touch her lunch at the numerous charity events she attended on a daily basis. While this might seem absolutely admirable, it became clear that the characters who repeatedly cropped up at these charity events were doing it just so they could be out to lunch, or to be seen in the 'right' crowds.

My services were always a topic of discussion. 'What would I do for the charity *free of charge.*' I'm not averse to giving to charity, but at that point in time, I was close to being a charity myself. I worked every hour I could find for every penny there was on offer. That said, I gave as much as I could with barely a thank you from The Snitch, and very little in the way of a kickback like a referral, or a nod towards some of her friends who might have wanted a PT. So, with the new studio opened, she was now someone else's issue.

Clients are always pushing boundaries to see what they can get – for free. The Snitch was no different. Even before she had suggested I offer my services to charity, she'd come to me initially with the idea that she was going to get a discount before she even knew what my prices were. As you can imagine, this didn't happen. She'd clearly never heard of L'Oreal – Because I'm Worth It. I'd later find out, however, that she resented this.

Regardless of the matter, she'd now come back into my life at a significant low point for me. My studio and I were struggling. What do I do? Do I take her back? Do I give her discount?

Her incoming message read a little something like this:

Hi Matt,

I hope you are well. I wanted to get in touch, to ask if I can come and see you at your new studio. The trainer they have given me here has hurt my ankle and I'm not happy. Please let me know a date and time and your new address so I can come in.

Kind regards,
The Snitch

I decided that my pride needed to be swallowed and I desperately needed the business, so I sent her dates and times and waited patiently for her to reply.

Then nothing. Nothing at all.

I call, I email, I text. No response. This was highly unusual.

She'd never stood me up before, or even missed a session. In times of stress like this I always start questioning myself. Have I done something wrong? Have I been out of order in anyway? What stupid foot in mouth thing had I said to put her off? Questions, questions, questions, but then I left it for a couple of days.

In the meantime, the metaphorical bath was beginning to overflow again.

And then, it overflowed.

I received a letter through the post from the lawyer of the owner of the old church gym. It turned out that the owner wanted to take me to court for breaching my contract on six different counts! I stood there reading the summons, flummoxed. My gut was spinning cartwheels; I had so many questions, I panicked. I read the letter again and again trying to understand what the hell I had done wrong. I called every confidant I knew, to try and appease my whirring mind.

I was being sued.

For emailing back Snitchy Snitcherson.

Un-fucking-believable.

The following few weeks I was in a near-constant state of panic. I had to find a decent solicitor, get my finances in order, and go over each point in its entirety, to see what they thought I had done.

Straightaway, I knew four out of the six accusations to be completely redundant. On one account I was being sued because I said I was going back into design and not PT. On a second account I was being sued because I couldn't work within a two-mile radius of one of their studios, rendering me unable to earn in London (which is considered unreasonable). They were farcical to say the least. However, the two that struck me the most, were the ones saying that I was soliciting clients and work colleagues (and they had proof).

I had friends at the former studio. I made it very clear that if they were to ever leave, they would have a studio where they could train their clients. Was this illegal? Should I have not said that? My mind was racing harder than a four-year-old to an ice cream van.

But the one that really stung, because I'd been so careful about, was soliciting clients. I hadn't, I'd been so careful, so what the hell was this about, and how did they have proof I asked myself.

It was time to lawyer up.

It was time to fight fire with fire.

And by fire, I mean money. Because, damn, solicitors are expensive!

The following months our solicitors exchanged letters at £200 per pop, until I'd amounted a bill of around £2,500. It didn't seem like it was going away, and I really didn't want the expense of it reaching the courts, so I had to get serious and hire a mega firm. A well-written £1,000 letter later, and the ex-employer/gym owner backed down, knowing they couldn't win in court on any of the counts that they had proposed.

It cost me, but the relief made me feel like the bathtub was now empty again. I could breathe. I might now be in debt, but I wasn't being consumed by that horrible feeling of being attacked.

During this process, I was told by my solicitor that I should refrain from speaking to any of my old colleagues, until it was all done and dusted. But once it was, it was time for them to know exactly what had happened. I wanted them to know the shit I was put through, and to warn them in case they might also find themselves in a similar situation. However, to my surprise, they all knew because I was being publicly made an example of, and the owner's 'rule of fear' over his employees and contractors was being spread out like butter.

Here's where it gets more interesting. In hard times, it's always good to know who your friends are. Thankfully, I still had some friends at the old church, and so I asked if they could do a bit of digging. I wanted to know what proof they had of my soliciting clients. And who ratted me out?

As it turns out, The Snitch had struck a deal with my ex-manager. In return for her getting me to offer her dates and times (that would be put down in writing), she would be given a discount on her PT sessions.

This little debacle, furthered by The Snitch, had cost me

nearly £3,500. She nearly lost me my new studio that I had spent a decade working towards. She nearly lost me my business. She tried to ruin my reputation for the sake of getting a few pounds off her PT sessions! As always, it's the richest most entitled clients looking for the biggest handouts.

For all of her hard work and effort The Snitch only received £10 off each of her PT sessions. A couple of years later, that gym closed its doors. She probably amounted to 40 sessions per year, which equates to a saving of £800 for the duration of the time that the gym stayed open. It cost me £3,500. Plus VAT.

Let it be known that while some people have 23 pairs of chromosomes, The Snitch has 666...

And they're all bastard poisonous.

PART FOUR

THE ALL ROUND KNOW-IT-ALL

LESSON FOUR:

Don't be another bollock faced foghorn of a dickhead with a podcast. Don't let a crustacean get the better of you. And don't lie about your abilities … otherwise you might end up with Legionnaires' disease!

My time as a PT has taught me many things. But the one thing that I have learnt that stands out above anything else, is that a PT is never ever wrong. I'm not sure what it is, or why, but PTs believe they are a walking-talking *University Challenge* on *everything*. We are the world's greatest psychologist, physiotherapist, relationship counsellor, and, as you've read, even a gynaecologist. There is no end to our talents. We just can't help but offer a solution, when actually the best thing to do is just say, 'I actually don't know.' It's almost like the ability to be wrong is not in our DNA.

By the end of 2015 I had a long list of high-paying clients, a ton of celebrities willing to put their health in my hands, and athletes wanting to know how I could push them to the next level. I was operating my own private studio and it was hard not to let my ego over inflate. Combine this with being inside your own fitness bubble, you don't see as many people as you once did, so you become insular. You rely on your own knowledge to get you through the sessions. You don't experience alternative ways of working, so over time you become everything you despise and swore you'd never become. In my case that was true, and things needed to change. After a bullshit lawsuit and a multitude of fractured clients (you're about to read about a couple of them) it was time to say goodbye to my ego and move on. Realising that I didn't need to own my own place to be a good trainer was one of the hardest and most costly lessons I learnt. Now that I am older, wiser and considerably greyer, I can look back now and see where I went wrong. The trainer I once was has gone. But, hey, I am not going to be completely self-deprecating, because the issues that I once presented are still rife in this industry.

Most personal trainers go out of their way to inflate their own sense of self and worth. It's as if their egos are hot air balloons constantly in need of re-inflating. Podcasts here, seminars there, and social media rants all over the place, when really they ought to be clocking up more hours on the actual gym floor before regurgitating what they *think* they know. The fitness industry is constantly changing; fads come and go, trends pass us by, and PTs have to be quick to adapt. But there are some PTs who stick to their mantra or dogma no matter what. There are a hundred ways to skin a cat, but few have the knife skills, and instead of the client being the priority, they care more about competing against other PTs. It's like everyone is trying to outdo or impress everyone else in the industry, and they forget the real reason why they're there – to serve the client. We've gone from being humble to complete 'significunts' (significant cunts'– you're welcome!)

But knowing everything isn't just reserved for PT parking spaces. Clients can be equally guilty of being a know-it-all. I'm sure that anyone who's had any longevity in this industry could reel off a fistful of clients who thought that they were right or had some silly notion of what it is they need to do and how to get there. To some, you really are just a facilitator. I'm sure these are the same people who'd take this approach with their lawyer or with their doctor: 'Sorry, Doc, you've got this wrong, my child will not have that measles vaccination, you will administer some Calpol, two lots of Panadol and some antihistamines and we'll be on our way.' Sadly, in some cases, I think they do.

So, this chapter is a nod to a few occasions where their know-it-all attitude got the better of them, and in one particularly embarrassing time, my own ego got the better of me.

Humility is about to ensue…

THE PRAWN

At the end of my first year of my owning my own studio, I realised I couldn't go on for much longer. The space I had was no bigger than a large box, and it was becoming difficult to make it work effectively. Having two other trainers and clients in at the same time was not going to work. I was footing the majority of the bills myself every month through savings and given that the accounts didn't reflect my growing client base, I was getting bored with feeling down about it. It was time to face up and realise that owning my own place wasn't what it was cracked up to be. At least, not then.

So, without much hesitation, I started to look at working at other gyms, paying the usual fees without the headache of all the admin and bills, or start investing in some mobile training gear and run some home training PT. I didn't really fancy doing either if I'm brutally honest. I felt like I'd lose the air of exclusivity, which was paramount to my brand. At the time I was feeling incredibly low mentally, so knowing I'd have to close everything I'd worked so hard for was a tough pill to swallow. I didn't want to feel, or look, like a failure, so I started coming up with hare-brained options that included me selling everything. I imagined going to work in a surf shop in Hawaii somewhere (it looked easy) or skipping the latest lease payment, changing my name and buggering off to a kibbutz. I even envisaged going back to live in my parents' garage and watching TV all day. I was clutching at straws. I just felt like I needed to run away.

Then came a lifeline. My lifeline.

Through all the work I had achieved within the celebrity sphere, I had become known for my success in 'body transformations'. Given that I was one of the first PTs in the UK to utilise hormone testing (consisting of blood work, urine, saliva and stool testing by clinics in Harley Street), I had a far deeper understanding of clients than your Average Schmo. Whilst it is a somewhat now redundant service, at the time I was ahead of the curve, and people were desperate to see the results.

For context, in 2021, a body transformation coach is one where you'd see extreme results. They are often facilitated by ex-stage competitors, who are in top shape themselves. While these are always great to see, the realities are often clouded in secrecy about what they eat, how they train, or what they 'use' – and, yes, I mean performance enhancers. Before 2010, however, the attainable physique was different to what it is today. For example, when I was a 'fitness model' the physique that was most commercial was more of a swimmer's build – wide shoulders, tapered waist with Brad Pitt show abs. Today's standards are more akin to an eighties action figure (think The Rock). Even today's female physiques are bigger and more ripped than their counterparts ten years ago.

Just when I was ready to pack it all in and join all the other wanker hipster fitness wannabes in Bali, I was approached by an agent about a film they were starting to shoot, where the actor had to be in 'martial arts shape' for the role.

Never one to turn down an opportunity, I agreed to take on this newly minted and newly famous actor as a client. The future Jean-Claude-Wham-Bam – let's call him 'Rocky' – was American but residing in London whilst the details of the film were being finalised. This gave him around three months to get in shape before filming started at Pinewood studios. They would then move on to filming on location in LA, which is where the client lived. The agent informed me that I would train Rocky daily for the first three months and then be on set for the London filming portion for another four more weeks, preparing meals, etc. Once the UK section of filming had concluded, his LA trainer would take over.

After a lot of negotiating with the management company (the actors never pay – it's their management that deal with the money) Rocky and I got down to business. This was a contracted job that required four month's commitment and I planned to close down my studio operations at the end of this one last job – just like the Hollywood trope. I would then flog all the equipment to people who had home gyms, and finally be free of it all.

I moved all my then-current clients over to a couple of trainers who I knew. If I got this job right, it would be the ticket to the Hollywood big leagues. I had been on film sets several times before and knew the potential opportunities that could come my way on top of the year's salary I would make in just four months. I would have been stupid to turn it down.

Not unlike many of the Americans who I've trained, Rocky knew exactly what he wanted. He was highly motivated and there wasn't much that was going to stop him in his path to getting there. But, before we started, I needed to 'liaise' with his current trainer. So, I set up a phone call.

'Hey, Mark,' came the soft nasal Los Angeles accent down the phone.

'It's Matt, but yes, hi, nice to meet you. How are you?' I asked, going through the motions of polite British small talk.

'Listen, bro, I'm gonna cut to the chase here. This client has trained with me for years now, we are in a good place and I don't want that messed up OK, like, you get my drift bro, OK?'

I was a little lost as to what to say. It was one of those times where you find yourself speechless. I had been caught off guard by the unexpected change of tone in our conversation.

He continued: 'I've not wasted my time getting him ready for this opportunity, just for someone who I don't know to come in and take the credit for it. I hope you understand, man? Are you a competitor yourself? Like, what are your diet protocols? What supplement companies do you endorse? Like, listen man, I've come too far to let this guy go. What methodology do you use when it comes to cardio? How many clients have you got, 'cause like, you know, like, you gotta get rid of them, man. I want you to focus. You gotta FOCUS!'

Before this phone call, I felt pretty pumped about this gig. But good moods are much like balloons – all it takes is one prick to spoil the fun.

'Hey, I understand your worries, "bro", but don't worry, I've got a lot of experience in this field,' I said in my too polite British accent. He cut me off short.

'Listen man, I don't care, I've got years of experience training pros on stage, actors and actresses in films. I'm the go-to guy out here, you know. I've got a pretty good rep around these parts, you know what I'm sayin'? Like, I'm the man around here.'

I thought this guy was a blockbuster dickweasel, a five-star fuck knuckle. However, I didn't rise to his bait. I played it cool and tried to get off the phone as quickly as possible.

'I'll send you updates of the workouts and the diet plans along the way, so you know what's been going on, OK,' I said reassuringly trying to end the call. He, however, wouldn't let it go.

'Like, I get that but, you know, I'm like a leading physique trainer, man,' he said inflating his ego by blowing his own dick. 'I need to know that you're doing the right job, man, like, give me something here. I don't think you're up to this challenge, like, it needs focus. REAL focus.'

I tried to sneak a word in edgeways, but he wasn't having any of it.

'Like, I'm the king out here, everyone knows who I am and my results, man. I've stepped on stage hundre......'

I put the phone down.

I started to Google this absolute sphincter squirrel immediately. Who is he really? Who has he worked with? What's his online status? How does he interact with clients/the public? All good things to note down before I compile an arsenal of verbal weaponry for our next call.

Lo and behold, this guy is a physique coach. He has a strong following and has some desirable before and after client shots. However, upon further inspection, a lot of them were of himself, but with the faces cut off. Now, every man and his dog is a 'fitness model'. I am that man with that dog. Anyone can get a great physique, hire a photographer to take a few shots, and BOOM they become a model. Well, not where I'm from. I had an agent, I had professional shoots which were paid for, and I regularly went to castings. Now all fitness models think they need a six pack, and a sun tan to be the next David Gandy. Imagine if they deleted their Instagram account and WALLOP, they're no longer a 'model'.

There's a name for these frauds: Prawns.

Why prawns, you might ask? Well, the only good thing about a prawn is the body, right? And our man in LA was a first-grade Prawn. I'll be damned if he thought this was my first rodeo.

Anyway, Rocky and I started working together. He was well versed in the main movements, so we skipped a lot of the relearning stuff and got in to the thick of it. All his diet was re-configured, his daily routines were logged and structured, and I checked in twice a day to make sure that he was on schedule.

I didn't send the Prawn anything.

For those who want to know, this was my schedule for Rocky. Feel free to skip ahead if it's of no interest.

5.15am – Pre Workout snack/hydration
5.30am – High Intensity Interval Training/30 minutes 4x per week
7.30am – Meal 1
8.30am-12pm – film prep
12pm – Meal 2
1pm-2pm – Sleep
2pm-3pm – Resistance training/x6 per week
3.30pm – Meal 3
4pm-7pm – Film prep, consisting of stunt and martial arts training
8pm – Long steady duration training/ 1-hour 4x per week
9.30pm – Meal 4

10.30pm – Meditation/Breathing techniques
11pm – Sleep

The diet part is too complicated to go into because it varied over the weeks leading up to filming (reduction of overall calories, reverse dieting and carb cycling). The point was that my routine was highly structured, with one day off a week for him to do as he pleased, and without my nagging ass getting on top of him.

After about six weeks of us working together, I had a distinct feeling that Rocky was starting to veer off course. It began when I noticed that he was not hitting the right macros (macronutrients – protein, carbohydrates and fats) in his meals, and then it swiftly moved on to him questioning the training plan. And pretty soon, it started to show. At first I thought nothing of it, but the more it happened the more it aggravated me; I had lost control.

And then it hit me.

The Prawn.

We were about two weeks out from filming, and about six weeks out from Rocky going back to LA. The Prawn knew that filming was about to start and had started to sabotage my strategy. He either wanted me to fail, or he wanted to exert some control over Rocky. Either way, it was fucking up all my good work. If the client was going into this film in great shape, then the Prawn wanted some recognition for it. It all started to make sense, so I brought it up with the client:

'Hey Rocky, what's Prawn's view on your training and your diet? I haven't heard from him in ages and wondered if you were still in contact,' I asked, knowing full well that given our phone conversation all those weeks ago, a character like the Prawn wouldn't just mind his own business.

Rocky looked at me slightly sheepish. Blood filled up his cheeks and he lost eye contact. 'I have to be honest, he's had quite a bit to say on the matter actually. He's a good guy, he means well, but, yeah, I guess you can imagine that he's got some strong views on a few of the things we are doing,' Rocky replied.

It turned out that the Prawn had tried to change almost everything we were doing. Alongside bad mouthing me and my knowledge, he also attempted to get the client to start eating six meals a day, do fasted cardio, and increase his anaerobic cardio, so that the resistance sessions were all out warfare. Basically, he wanted to overload the client into exhaustion by expending as many calories as possible in the quickest amount of time = drastic fat/weight loss.

This was not how I worked. Why? Because it doesn't generate the best results at all. It's a short cut, at best, dangerous, at worse.

Rocky's body fat had reduced, but he'd also lost size and shape. Anyone can lose weight if they expend too many calories, that's a given. But to lose fat AND maintain muscle needs good consistent structure. The Prawn was fucking things up, and Rocky was listening to him and being sheepish about it.

With filming now just a week away, I would normally have my client carb cycling and drying him out (dehydrating the body so it looks 'drier' on camera), but instead I was loading him with carbs so he looked fuller. It was the only saving grace for him not to look 'skinny ripped'. Prior to this, I'd had a sit down meeting with one of the producers and the actors management company, citing my views on the past three months of training. They weren't entirely happy as to how he looked, but they agreed that the Prawn's influence was to blame (they'd had previous encounters with him), and they promptly ended their agreement with the mighty mollusc, citing that I would be taking the reins of training in LA.

This of course didn't go down too well with the Prawn. The day after I received a phone call.

'Yo, Mark, what's been up, man?' he began, trying to win me over. 'I heard you've been talking to Zzzz - you shouldn't have done that, man. I know what I'm doing, man. If you'd have stuck to my plan, he woulda been in much better shape. Things are gonna change, you know whatimsayin'?'

I'd had enough of this tool. 'No. I honestly don't know what you're saying,' I said. 'The management were unimpressed with your interference –'"bro" –' and now they've let me have control and pick up the pieces. You're finished.'

'Get tha hell outta here, man. Things gonna change when he's back. let me tell you. Like, you're a fake trainer, man. You ain't got shit on me…..'

I put the phone down, again.

By now, I was prepared to get my scuba diving gear on and go fight this fucker at the bottom of the ocean while all the other crustaceans looked on.

And, in four short weeks I'd have my chance to fight him. My flights were booked, and with the UK shoot at an end, it was time for a good old Californian showdown at dawn.

Man Vs Prawn.

It was a hot spring day when I arrived at LAX airport. I'd travelled with half of the film's crew who I'd befriended over the weeks of London filming. I and two others were booked into a private residency, slightly north of Hollywood, in a beautiful spot in the Tarzana hills. I was to stay there for the next four weeks overseeing our actor's training routine and diet and to generally keep an eye on him.

That was until about a week in, when the worst that could have happened, happened. Still being stiff from the flight, and being overzealous on the deadlift, I found myself in bed, in agony. A searing, almost internal pain resonated all across my lower spine like someone had taken a sledgehammer and battered my lower back like Annie in Steven King's *Misery*. I couldn't stand up even if I tried. I genuinely thought I had broken my back. Filled with worry, anxiety and the inability to work, I knew my time in LA was limited and the management company wasted no time in getting me some ridiculously strong painkillers. I knew I was in trouble, the management company knew I was in trouble, and there was only one other option for their client, Rocky. Just when I thought it couldn't get any worse, they brought back the Prawn.

As I lay on the floor in the bedroom of the Tarzana house, with the rest of the crew working around me like I was some sort of leprosy victim, I was made aware that the Prawn was coming to take over where I'd left off. As my heart sank, knowing my work here was done, I tried to tell myself that the most noble thing to do would be to co-operate as much as possible. Just kidding. There would be no co-operation. This was now his circus, and these were his monkeys.

That's when I heard the jumped-up tones of the Prawn enter the house. 'So, you're Mark,' he said. 'The tables have turned, bro.'

He knew full well my name wasn't fucking Mark.

'You know, karma has a way of working things out. Like, dude, this was never your gig,' he said walking around the room like a detective solving a crime. 'I always knew I'd get the last word on this. You tried hard and you lost, Mark, but this was my show, like, really, you should be paying me for all the work I now have to undo. I was always gonna win this one, dude. No one gets the better of me.'

I was still lying on the floor like a beached whale unable to get up to beat this turbo gimp upside the head. He looked at me with a smirk on his face:

'Goddamnit, you need to smile more, Mark,' he said, thinking he was the boss.

'You need to fuck off more,' I replied, daring my body to get up off the floor. With that, he left.

The following day the management company booked me an emergency flight home and whisked me straight in to see a spine specialist in London. I didn't even get a chance to say goodbye to Rocky, but by this point I was humiliated and in extreme pain due to my two new delightful sequestered (slipped) herniated discs. I didn't care.

A year later, Rocky's film didn't do well at the box office. But the actor went on to become a household name in a TV show. The last time I saw the Prawn's face was on his YouTube channel where he posts videos showing off his subhuman strength in the squat and deadlift, putting up some seriously high numbers.

However, the all-round know-it-all's ego eventually got the better of him. Not so long after his YouTube videos were launched, it was leaked that the Prawn had used fake weights and he soon became the laughing stock of the industry.

And just like prawns themselves, he proved himself to have

no guts, no spine and a head full of shit.

ROW, ROW, ROW, YOUR BOAT GENTLY DOWN THE STREAM

The consistent interval of melodious beeps sounded around me, echoing off the empty pea green ward walls. Doctors in their blue robes walked in twos with their clipboards pressed firmly against their chests. Nurses stood idly chatting to each other by the ward's reception, nonchalantly glancing my way – no doubt acknowledging how utterly feeble I looked in my ward gown with my socks on. If there's ever a time when you can completely strip away someone's dignity, it's when they're in a hospital gown.

I sat upright in the bed, cubicle curtains drawn. I look around bleary-eyed when a nurse with a crooked nose came over to check my blood pressure.

'How are you feeling, Mr Hodges? You still look a little peaky. Your temperature is up. Still feeling sick?' the nurse asked, whilst simultaneously writing on a clipboard.

'When can I get out of here?' I said, looking at my watch like I had better things to do.

'We're just waiting on your results and then you can go,' she told me, as another doctor came over to take her attention away.

I was no stranger to hospitals. I'd spent a lot of time in them when I was a kid – suspected meningitis and appendicitis were all on the list of my on-going pubescent ailments. After my Hollywood debacle, I became a regular in the private hospital sector with the two herniated discs I'd suffered in LA.

Why was I here this time? Well, let me tell you ...

Things had not worked out in LA as I had hoped, so I knew that I needed to get back into the PT game. Even with an agonising back injury, I knew I needed to work and get some of my clients back. While most of them had moved on, I found a few who were keen to return. The only issue now was that I had no studio, and no equipment. So I got back in touch with the owner of The Cave to see if they had room for me. Luckily, it had new owners and had been completely revamped with a new investor, new interior and a bigger budget. The dank, damp dripping walls and overflowing toilets were a thing of the past. This place was much more attractive to future clients, I hoped.

Luckily, I'd landed on my feet, again.

However, now knowing what I knew about the game, I wanted to build my business back up, but this time branch out a bit more. At the time, Irish had found a new residence in southwest London, and he invited me down to train (well, when I say train, I could only do as much as someone with a spine crippling injury could do).

After a bit of research, the southwest felt like it had some good spaces and a ton of clients who were rich with time and motivation. The city's southwest is also home to many of London's most famous rowing houses, which adorn the banks of the Thames.

I enjoyed the new gym that Irish was working at, and it didn't take me long to ask if he could pull a favour and get me working as one of their freelancers so I could spread the business across both north and south west London.

'Oh, Jaysus loves ya, Matty. Oi will do me best, Horse,' he

said.

It's good to have friends in this game. After a couple of informal chats, I was taken on, but I still needed to find my own clients. So, you're in the rowing capital of the UK, with every boathouse generally open to the public – what do you do?

You go back to basics.

I leafletted the hell out of all of them and made damn sure I hit the bigger ones first. Now, at the time, the majority of these institutes would have had their own strength and conditioning coaches. However, much like Premiership football clubs (I did a little stint with a few players at a top four Premiership club, which you'll learn about later), I knew that often the S&C coaches, the kit men and the team reps were all mates of mates, the uncle's neighbour's son sort of vibe. They were closed networks, who'd employ internally, often resulting in the athletes looking elsewhere for better quality training or therapy.

Fortunately for me, I had two female master rowers who wanted specialised training.

BOOM, I'm in.

Now at the time, my stepbrother was dating my future sister-in-law, who just so happened to be an Australian Olympic rower who'd competed in the 2012 London Olympics. What better person to get an insight as to the rowers' real regimes, programmes and nutrition? After chewing her ear off about technique, ergometers and time splits, I felt like a new man. A man who could take on the world. A man who could get in a single scull and row to America if he wanted to (remember this is in an umbrella chapter about egos). It was time to train these rowing pros.

Not unlike many new clients, the analysis I'd go through with each of them was reciprocated. They wanted to know about my experience, the results I'd had, and the qualifications I had attained. Whilst this was fairly plain sailing (I annoyingly still couldn't show before/afters of previous clients due to NDAs), I did feel somewhat overwhelmed. I remember at the time feeling like I wasn't pushing the athlete specific training as much as I could have, and I thought both the girls were after some hot shot

Olympian trainer. Instead, they got a broken backed, grey in his thirties, average PT. What was I to do?

Well, the only option was to go to the default postgraduate personal trainer handbook, and pretend I knew everything about everything – the 'all round know-it-all'. Sometimes you just have to go back to what you know, or think you know.

'Yes, of course I've been in a boat. We should go out sometime,' I'd said, hoping that they wouldn't say yes …

And, of course, they did say yes.

Over the coming weeks, I made every excuse not to go near the boat shed other than to complete the compulsory Level 0 (basic safety) and to train the two girls. I'd miraculously have a client or a 'meeting' directly after their sessions just so I could leave the vicinity as quickly as possible. However, this was a ticking time bomb because what does every athlete love to do? The sport they love of course. And the more people they can get involved, the better it makes them feel, especially if it means showing they are bigger, stronger and faster than their trainer.

I was in a pressure cooker of six-foot females in spandex, with broad shoulders and an ambition to compete against their gender counterparts. There was no way out of this, and a date was finally arranged for me to get in a two-seater.

Over the weeks leading up to the row, I was frantically calling my future sister-in-law, Googling what to expect, trying to find out the terminology that rowers use, just so I didn't look like a complete wafflemeister. When the time had come, I was well versed in what to expect, and it was now just a case in trying to pull it off.

It was time to bite the bullet.

On the day of reckoning, we were due to get in the boat at around 7am, before the traffic on the river was busy, and when the swell was calm. I'd got up early to psych myself up and do a multitude of mobility exercises so that my broken back could at least move like that of a thirty-something. The sun shone brightly overhead, shimmering off the ripples of the Thames. Birds danced their flight over the treetops, dive-bombing for the early worm, whilst squirrels emerged from the bushes to forage for buried treasure. The air was clean with a slight dew over the tips of the green spring grass. It was one of those mornings where there was a slight chill to the air, but the blue sky made you feel like it was summer.

I was shitting myself.

After a short walk from my apartment (the same apartment the socialite had lived in), I made my way down to the boat yard to be accosted by my two clients and a couple of the other girls in their team. They were awkwardly manoeuvring boats out of the shed, propping them up on their wide shoulders whilst they trudged their wellies down the slope and into the water. I knew that this was when most rowers hurt their backs, so I made my excuses and refrained from lifting anything until the coxed tub pair boat was put into the water – look at me impressing you with the terminology, right? (A coxed tub pair is a fatter width boat for two people and a cox. Both rowers have two oars).

So, the boat was in the water, one of my clients' friends was cox, and one of the clients I was training was sitting at the back of the boat calling me to come down the slope and into the, soon to be, death dinghy.

Now, I'm going to make an excuse here. When your back feels like it's broken and you're about as mobile as a granny on a Zimmer frame, any uneven surface is going to cause you problems. To get you to try and understand what this feels like, try and visualise this; a big cast iron anvil balancing on a toothpick. Any tiny movement and the toothpick cannot hold the weight so it breaks, or it moves, and causes you an incredible amount of pain. This is what a slipped disc feels like.

As you well know by now, I'm not one to let a challenge get the better of me and I'm already way too invested in this to just call it a day. The way I saw this day going was just a set of challenges I had to conquer:

1) Wake up, don't bail.
2) Get to the boat shed, don't bail.
3) Get from the shed to the water, don't fall.
4) Get into the boat, don't fall.

5)   Use an immense amount of upper body strength to try and persuade the girls you know what you're doing and can control a boat. Don't fall.

6)   Enter into the Oxford vs. Cambridge boat race because you're now a pro.

By now, I'd accomplished the first two stages and I hadn't bailed. Number three was relatively easy, however, I must have looked like Bambi on ice trying to get down the slope, as I was trying desperately not to jolt the toothpick.

Number 4 – get in the boat and don't fall. This is harder than you think, but luckily the tub boat was thicker and therefore easier to balance on. I got in and sat down on the most uncomfortable dilapidated wooden seat ever. I was sure I'd be tweezing splinters out my arse for the next couple of weeks.

'You alright there?' The cox asked me, suspiciously eyeing up my inability to get comfortable.

'Yeah, I'm fine, just not used to these sort of boats, you know …?' I replied, hoping that she'd think I had some savoir-faire about me.

The cox nodded to my client and we started pushing ourselves off the banks and into the main stream of the river. At this point I was about to go into stage five when I realise the one crucial thing to rowing is something I may well have missed out on. No number of phone calls to Australia was going to get me out of this one.

They're called oars.

Fucking big, long wooden things that weigh a ton, and are bastard hard to use.

We started paddling out and I was already finding them difficult. I'd already smacked the client's oars behind me with my own. I wasn't timing anything right, and I was either missing the water which threw me back and almost off the seat, which was still throwing needles up my arse. No matter how strong you are, if you're technique isn't right, you're going to fail. Stage Five upper body strength needed re-thinking. We slowed down and I started to find my rhythm.

After about twenty minutes, with both girls realising this was indeed my first time in a boat, we slowed down into a steady pace where I've finally got the tempo in accordance with my pair. I was getting the hang of it, and after about forty minutes we were gliding past other crews. Then, the worst thing that could have been said to me came from my client sat behind me, who, through laboured breathing shouted:

'Matt, you're a natural at this, you should sign up!'

What? What was that? Did I just hear someone say that I'm amazing at this? I should go faster did you say? You what … did you just say that you wanted to race every other squad out here?

I'm very aware that those voices in my head aren't real, but sometimes, just sometimes, their ideas are awesome.

With that, I suddenly changed the flow and dipped my oars deeper into the water to get more purchase. The upper body challenge from stage five was now doable …

Except, if you're going to go hard you better know what you're doing.

Next thing I know, I've missed the water with the oar on my right, which hurled me sideways. In the blink of an eye, I let go of the right oar trying to secure myself to the side of the boat as I topple sidewards. The cox let out a scream, the client behind me tried to grab me, but it was all too late.

SPLASH.

The impact of freezing cold water hit me to the core, sending an electric bolt up through my back. Dirty brown water shot up my nose and down the back of my throat, making me choke on the fetid rat piss of Thames water. The odd gargling of water filled my ears, mixing with it the shouts from the girls on the boat. The raw blisters on my hands from the oars start to sting. But nothing hurt more than my broken ego.

I was about two metres away from the boat (training had taught me to find my way back to safety). Luckily a good dose of adrenaline had taken my back pain away (maybe I should lose my shit more often), and I climbed back into the boat smelling like old socks and dysentery.

We went immediately back to the boathouse. I took a

shower and tried to rid my body of the noxious sewage-contaminated Thames water I'd just bathed in, while the girls filed the necessary documentation that was required when someone falls from a boat.

After everything was ticked off and accounted for, we went to the bar to discuss the day's events over a stiff drink. Not one to be a glass half empty, I finally admitted I was no Steve Redgrave and put my professional rowing career behind me. The girls, now knowing we were perfectly fine, thought this the height of hilarity and every Tom, Dick and Harry who came into the bar were informed of the events that had unfolded. I'm no stranger to having the piss ripped out of me at the best of times, given I'd worked with Danger and Co, but this clique soon made me the unwitting rowing club fool for the day. Although I did get a few sympathy drinks, to be fair.

That was, until about an hour in, after what I now learn to be called 'catching a crab' (mistiming the oar stroke so that it hits you), when the multitude of drinks started to hit me. I suddenly started to feel a little odd. My stomach was churning like I hadn't eaten for days ... and then suddenly I needed the toilet. Like, NOW.

In the time it took to get from the bar to the gents, I had gone from sitting comfortably, laughing off the smell of rat urine, to a full throttle, out the nose, burn the back of your throat, stomach bending, ab-crushing puke fest. I felt like my body wanted to turn inside out with a crushing headache that dropped me to the floor. If I hadn't had looked sorry for myself coming back to shore, then going to the bar to tell the girls something was seriously wrong must have looked quite the picture.

Within thirty minutes I was in A&E at Charing Cross Hospital, with a metal bowl by my side with suspected 'Thames Tummy', a diagnosis which can lead to hepatitis, salmonella or worse, Legionnaires' disease, believe it or not. I spent the next day feeling sorry for myself looking at the pea green walls, and constantly bugging the nurses about when I could leave. To say I was keen to see the back of this debacle would be an understatement. I wanted out and so did my now battered ego.

Luckily, I kept training the girls. One went on to win gold at the World Masters Championships (most people's real results go further than a before and after picture) and the other, strangely, ended up becoming one of the best aesthetical transformations I ever achieved.

Did I ever step back in a boat? Did I bollocks! Rowing is one of those sports I'll scrub off as 'been there, done that, and got the muck-stained t-shirt' to prove it.

So, this story and the final part of this chapter, is for all of you out there who think they can get away with being a smart-ass know-it-all like I used to be. The all-round know-it-all falls on both sides and will almost certainly, almost definitely, almost always, come back to bite you in the ass.

Or, as in my case, puke your insides out and get splinters up your bum.

PART FIVE

MYSTICAL HOLISTICAL

LESSON FIVE:

Don't ever, ever, ever, ever say that breast-feeding in public is like GBH to the eyes.

We now move on to what I consider the most fucked-up part of the health and fitness industry and the ever-growing behemoth that is the 'wellness' industry. In the past few years, there has been a real shift in eco-sustainability, where conscious buying is becoming a priority. This would be welcomed if it wasn't for the marketing moguls, who bring out their flip charts and get together to discuss different ways of how they can rape and pillage wellness for only their benefit.

So, here we are, on the cusp of something I personally find quite frightening.

Today, we are dealing with an epidemic of overly self-conscious consumers who would rather not vaccinate themselves, or their children, and believe they have every intolerance going or have turned to veganism, without really understanding what being vegan is truly all about. This also happened to the yoga market fifteen years ago, where hundreds of thousands of people started yoga in the UK because it was considered fashionable without understanding the ethos or the purity of the art. I can't help but feel 'wellness' has been co-opted and bastardized into a term that just means scare-mongering consumers with things that are not only non-sustainable … but then charge you a fortune for it.

My point is perfectly illustrated in a place that I worked at for many years, since 2016; a small studio above a health food store aptly titled Planet Organic (the UK owned equivalent to Whole Foods).

So, let me paint a picture for you …

The moment you walk into Planet Organic, you know where you've found yourself. The pungent earthy smell of vitamins and minerals, the pop-up stands with eco-friendly, biodegradable, gluten free chocolate bites (for which customers pay 300 per cent over the wholesale rate). People around you sport the alt-left self-beacon of green and purple hair, there are the breast feeders in one corner and eco-warriors sporting tie-dye in the other. A place where it wouldn't be uncommon to see a 'Trustafarian' (a middle class trust fund eco warrior likely found with dreadlocks) playing the guitar with friendship beads around his neck (thank you to *The Inbetweeners* for that one).

OK, I'm being massively unfair and stereotypical, but you can picture what kind of place this is, right? The sort of place you'll find a two hundred and fifty million year old Himalayan rock salt that has a sell by date on it.

But, I'm going to caveat this with the people who I met there on a daily basis. Given that this book is a combination of both the state of fitness affairs, and the people I've met along the way, it wouldn't be right if I didn't dedicate a chapter to this topic. The people who came through those doors had me in stitches. All. The. Fucking. Time. They are unwittingly funny in their conforming unconformity.

Let's start with Freddie …

FREDDIE

'I want everyone to breathe in slowly through your diaphragm, hold the pose for two seconds and then slowly exhale, counting to ten on the way down. I hope everyone is finding their Chakras releasing the negative energy they're holding? Good, good, now everyone relax, take a lie down on your backs and listen to the soothing music while you concentrate on your breathing. Namaste.'

Freddie's yoga sessions were always full, with a varying range of male and female participants, all there to relax and unwind to Freddie's soft croaky purr.

In her early twenties, Freddie was the type of girl who, through private education – naturally – never decided what she wanted to do in life, so upon doing the usual post-university year off travelling vibe she'd 'found herself' and started practising the art of yoga. At 5ft 9in, Freddie was a beautiful, leggy, big blue eyed, curly brown hair wayward type who wore long cotton shawls and a multitude of beautiful Indian silver bangles that adorned her slightly tanned arms. The contradiction between her look and her temperament was always something I found at odds. She dressed like she was meant to be the daughter of Shiva, all serene and zen, but instead she was high energy, cheeky and seemed more at home at a Zumba class than yoga.

I had recently left the establishment that Irish had introduced me to. I'd had a disagreement with the owner and a few of the wankpuffin trainers there which gave me no option but to look further afield. And so I found a nice little movement studio on top of Planet Organic. Previously having cut my teeth in one-to-one boutiques that focussed mainly on weight training, the new studio was a bit of a shock to my system.

A large, high ceilinged open space, it comprised a yoga studio and calisthenics gym and it was a thoroughfare of people who would gladly sit all day in Planet Organic, drinking Matcha tea and munching on overly processed soy protein bars. There were more than double the number of yoga teachers to PTs. Being the first of its kind in the area, the place was now a hotspot for the true purist yoga type. There were no athleisure-wearing, 'champagne at brunch' types here. It was a hardcore, Sanskrit writing, meditative chanting, mandala tattooed yoga fest, and leading from the front was young Freddie.

Now, normally in these situations, anyone who wasn't a yoga type could be seen a mile off. I, with my branded t-shirt, tracksuit bottoms and Nike trainers must have looked like Nelson Mandela at a National Front meeting. It wasn't the first time I had felt a little out of my depth but, to her credit, Freddie introduced herself quickly and showed me around, dispelling any negative transference that my body was emitting.

We instantly hit it off, with her falling into the role of my younger sister, and me being the older know-it-all, take no shit, bigger brother. We were both, very quickly, at a point where we felt comfortable enough to start taking the mick out of each other's practices. Freddie gave as good as she got, but because I was fond of her, she'd regularly push her luck and take the piss. I assumed these save-the-earth types didn't have a sense of humour; I thought they lived with their heads in the clouds. I was wrong.

After I'd found the groove with new clients and new timetables, Freddie and I would often find ourselves first to open up the studio with her taking the first class and me making sure that everything was in order so she didn't get in trouble. At around 8am we'd both have a break and head down into Planet Organic for breakfast. No matter where we were, no matter if we were in session, lazing about in the reception area or upstairs, or having food together, Freddie always brought with her a small bag of non-salted almonds, a sequined purse and a beaker full of apple juice (it's important to remember this).

The owner of this studio – I'm going to refer to him as 'Mr Horror' – always walked around with a look on his face like someone had killed his dog or spat in his food and was also a personal trainer. However, he was not a PT. He was a 'movement coach' and God forbid anyone who called him a PT, because you'd be thrown a look of deep disdain. But underneath the man-bun and Vivo Barefoot trainers, he was still a PT. And he knew it.

After about a month of working at the studio Mr Horror was chewing my ear off about something at reception when a huge whiff of urine wafted through the yoga studio doors as a customer left to get something from one of the lockers. It was a violation of my senses, it was that bad. We weren't in a council estate stairwell, we were in a posh middle class gym. Oh, sorry, 'movement studio'.

If it weren't for the fact that Mr Horror had a permanent look like he had a dirty sanchez under his nose, I'd have thought he had smelt it himself.

'What on earth is that smell? Can you smell it?' I asked, pointing my question at the owner.

He looked up from his computer: 'No, what is it?'

I lowered my tone and whispered over the reception table, 'It smells like piss, mate. Has that client pissed herself?' I asked, as I try to subtly nod over to the client retrieving things out of her locker. Bear in mind I'm no stranger to clients wetting themselves.

'No, I can't smell anything,' he said, looking back at his computer screen.

Well, I bloody could. And I can smell bullshit a mile away too. It was so strong that if Mr Horror couldn't smell it then he was either lying, trying to ignore it, or he had gone nose-blind.

I looked to the sky in amazement and took a peek through the yoga door window. Freddie was about to take a class with her bag of nuts and apple juice by her side, and for the life of me I couldn't see if anyone was sitting in a pool of urine. I scrubbed that one off thinking it must be an issue with the toilets.

Over the next few weeks, I noticed that salt deodorants and non-perfumed shampoos tended to make most people smell like stale milk, so I was starting to get used to the aroma of the place. The combined bouquet of earthly vitamins and body odour was starting to pay council tax in my nose cavities, and I thought nothing of it when the smell of urine became a regular feature.

That was until I received a hug from Freddie that I can only describe as a shaking down of a used Huggies nappy.

What the actual fuck? This chick absolutely stinks. She's my pal, I know she gets away with murder, I know she has hairy armpits, but not even she could get away with this. And then it dawned on me that every time I smelt the odious aroma of urine, it was normally when Freddie had been around. What do I say to my new pal that wouldn't be offensive or hurt her feelings? Nothing I could do or say would come out well, so, unlike the next story in this chapter, I decided to keep my mouth shut. A rarity I know.

Bringing up the issue with Mr Horror and the rest of the gang was quite frankly useless. I needed someone who was like a pig in truffle season, to seek out what was going on here. So, who do you think I brought in to cut through the ammonia?

Danger, of course.

Within a week of me telling him about the new place and what sort of vibe it had, he'd made his way from North London, down past the river and into my new territory. As you all now know there is no bigger fan of the female race than Danger and he has the receipts to prove it. Being told there might be another female wetting herself inside a gym only motivated him to get there quicker than an alcoholic to Oktoberfest. However, I didn't tell him the real reason why I wanted him there.

After a quick tour of the studio, we waited downstairs in the Planet Organic restaurant knowing that Freddie would soon be in to start her post-lunch session. We hurriedly chowed down on some organic hummus and gluten free flatbread before making our way upstairs to the foyer/reception area to await my dear friend Ms Pissypants.

'What you gonna do when she arrives?' I asked Danger, knowing I probably didn't want to know the answer.

'Nama-st(e)ick-it-in-her,' he replied.

I shouldn't have asked.

After a few minutes of idle chitchat between Danger, Mr Horror and me, I heard Freddie doing the rounds downstairs, saying hello to everyone she passed along the way. A 'Namaste' here, a 'Namaste' there, before she finally reached the top deck where we were all sitting.

'Hey, Matty,' Freddie bellowed at full volume. She'd got the attention of everyone at the reception area. In true Freddie fashion, she was sporting her usual dilettante clobber, alongside her bag of nuts and her apple juice. Freddie was quite possibly the most tactile female I'd ever known (which I knew would go down well with Danger), so after a round of huge filled up nappy hugs, I waited for Danger to do his bit and fall head over heels in love with her.

Instead, he looks fairly nonplussed and carried on observing the reception. We all made idle chat, when Freddie starts to have a private conversation with Mr Horror about the upcoming class. Danger took this as his opportunity to whisper in my ear.

'Boods, what the fuck is up with this one. Nice girl, but she stinks,' he said with a slight grimace on his face.

You can always rely on a pig to find the truffles.

As we both looked at her, I leaned my head into his earshot. 'I know, mate, I've been wondering about it for weeks. I mean, this lot generally get away with no deodorant, but for the life of me she smells like she's pissed herself and forgot to flush.'

We both shared a look of disgust as we continued to watch the Namaste queen hold court. As she sat down, Danger sidled himself up next to me. Freddie noticed Danger's reaction.

'Don't worry, honey, I won't bite,' she said laughing to herself, whilst taking a few nuts from her bag.

'Oh, no I'm not worried about that, love,' Danger said loudly. When no one was listening, he got a sneaky word in my ear: 'I'm more worried about getting a urinary tract infection,' he said wide-eyed.

About ten minutes before Freddie's yoga class was due to start, Mr Horror announced that we were no longer allowed to take food and drink into either of the studios. It had been a point of contention over the last few weeks but given that he'd noticed Freddie chowing down on some blanched almonds, he thought this was a good opportunity to bring up the subject.

'Guys, I know some of you have been taking food and drink into the studios and I just want to say that you can't do that anymore. A couple of the clients have complained, and it doesn't set a very good example,' he said, directing the point of the comment toward Freddie.

She'd now finished the almonds, and her class was about to start, but she still had her whole beaker of apple juice to finish. She looked at Mr Horror and pleaded with him that it was only a beaker and was no different to trainers taking bottled water into the sessions.

She had a fair point.

'No, no, no, no, *NO*. It was only last week I had to clear up some spilled fluid from the wooden floors. Please finish that here, Freddie. Water, yes, apple juice, no.' God forbid anyone that crossed Mr Horror's eyebrows when he'd told you to do something. There was no way out for poor old Freddie this time.

'Oh, for fuck's sake,' she muttered under her breath. Mr Horror heard.

'Listen, Freddie, if you don't like the rules then you don't need to be here,' he continued, trying to assert some form of authority. By now we could all sense that he'd grown tired of Freddie pushing her luck.

'Alright, alright,' she said smirking at Danger and me.

We're both sitting there watching this act of defiance with interest. Here we have the studio owner, who at the best of times wasn't the easiest bloke to get on with vs. Freddie, a young, immature, cheeky lass, but the most popular teacher at the studio.

Danger nudged me with his elbow to say, 'It's about to kick off'. But the fool mistook me for someone who didn't love the banter as much as he did. I already had front row seats!

Instead, Freddie, with her big blue eyes directly focussed on Mr Horror, lifted the beaker up to eye level, and looked at the half litre container of apple juice.

'Well, now I'm going to have to bloody down this aren't I?' she said.

Both Danger and I, breaking the tension in the room, began to chant: 'Down it, down IT, DOWN IT!'

Freddie, delighted that we were behind her in this act of contumacy, started to undo the top of the beaker.

And then it hits us all.

The smell of urine permeated the reception area, like a cat taking a shit on the kitchen counter on a hot day. The smell was so bad Danger retched into his own mouth. I nearly puked. And Mr Horror, well, he had a look of horror on his face even more horror-filled than normal.

The beaker wasn't full of apple juice.

It was full of urine.

Actual piss.

And, then, well, you can guess what happened next.

Freddie downed the entire beaker of piss.

When it was almost all gone, a light amber coloured liquid dribbled down the side of her mouth. She wiped it with her hand and then looked at the three of us.

'What, guys? Come on now, it's good for you,' she happily stated as she offered the backwash remains of her beaker to me.

I was too busy gagging and retching to say anything.

'I've been doing this for the last two months,' she said. 'Urophagia has cleaned my skin up no end. Come on, guys, it's good for you, try some.' She offered the beaker around like a bong at a frat party.

'Boods, I'm out.' And off Danger waltzed. Even he has a line he can't cross.

Mr Horror was still in horror and backed out of the room as if it was on fire. I was left sitting there with Freddie the pisshead doing my best to untangle myself from the situation.

'Freddie … what … the … actual … fuck are you doing?' I

asked her, sick to my stomach.

'Matty, trust me, I read this study months ago about urophagia. It's meant to be really good for you … if you do it properly, of course. Most people get it wrong and it hurts their kidneys, but if you do everything natural, make sure your diet is good, you keep hydrated then mother earth goes back into your body and revitalises you from the inside.'

I opened my mouth, but sentences seemed to be stuck in the back of my throat.

Freddie, beaker in hand, started ushering the gathering crowd into the yoga studio, when suddenly Mr Horror jumped up out of his chair and grabbed Freddie by the arm.

'Er, Freddie, I've told you, no drinking in the studio, I'm not going through this again.'

'Alright calm down, Gandhi,' Freddie said.

At that point, another client who was eager to get into the studio hurried past Mr Horror and bumped into Freddie's arm with her yoga mat.

In what seemed like slow motion, the beaker suddenly golden-showered Mr Horror's arm. Freddie put her hand to her mouth, hiding her own abhorrence as the beaker hit the floor bouncing around a couple of times emptying itself of female waste.

Mr Horror looked at me, like someone who had just lost the World Cup final to a VAR penalty. Now, knowing the magnitude of what has happened, he turned back to Freddie utterly defeated.

This was the beginning of the end for Freddie. Mr Horror went mental. A full-tilt breakdown. He was at his wit's end over Freddie's waste, but he was essentially castrated as he couldn't let her go because of how much business she brought in.

Over the days and weeks that followed this debacle, Freddie became increasingly obstinate. Given that most of her clients now knew she was drinking her own piss, her classes started to dwindle, and eventually she saw sense and ditched the piss water for real apple juice.

Freddie poured herself a half-litre of apple juice every time she came in just so she could wind up Mr Horror. Upon seeing her with her beaker full (of what he thought to be her own piss), he yet again flew into a tirade about drinking in classes only to find out the reality when Freddie jokingly pretended to spill it on the floor of the studio.

It was fair to say that these two were at breaking point. She would often confide in me that she'd had enough of the place and wanted to move on. It was fair enough, she was in her early twenties and she was entrenching herself deeper into the yoga life. Bar the urine beaker, she was pushing her luck in other areas of her work every time Mr Horror wasn't manning the studio. But her actions weren't going unnoticed, and about a month after the urine geyser incident, Mr Horror let Freddie go.

Not unlike many trainers in this industry, we often have fleeting moments of friendship. When people move on, we only ever end up seeing them on social media or occasionally we get to see them again at another studio. However, in Freddie's case she moved to Indonesia and we lost touch. She was well missed at the studio, but she wasn't the last person to ever do anything utterly disgusting there or get away with murder.

I very rarely ever see her updates on Instagram, but I know for one thing that still holds true – wherever she is, she's still taking the piss.

DO YOU WANT MILK WITH THAT?

I t was around the time of Freddie's departure that I began my first session of the day at 5am. It was safe to say I was in a bad mood, given that my first three clients were complete 'mood-hoovers'. My first one had already exhausted me with their complaint about the lack of recycling in an area where recycling was supposedly at the forefront of the local council's 'sustainable economic moral compass.'

My next client moaned for the entire session about how she couldn't park her new Land Rover because the wing mirrors were too small. By the third one, my mental health was hanging out my occipital region, so I forced myself to take a break. Limited by choice I ventured downstairs to Planet Organic to grab a coffee and eat some of their 'gluten free, spunk water quinoa porridge'. I plonked my weary ass down to eat the frog spawn they called porridge, when in came the yummy mummy brigade, crying kids and babies in tow.

What was about to happen next wasn't unusual for Planet Organic. This happened every single day, but today I wasn't going to let anything slide (apart from the porridge, of course).

To my surprise, (given that there were ample opportunities to *not* sit directly next to me) two women and their new-borns promptly decided that this was *exactly* where they were going to sit.

All I wanted was to stretch my legs.

All I wanted was a little peace before my next client.

All I wanted was to enjoy a normal porridge with normal milk, in a normal cup, with a normal spoon, but nooooooo … 'Tonsie Brinkleworth-Dudley' and her annoying incarnation had to step on in and ruin the party.

So, what do most women do when they have a hungry crying baby in tow? Feed them of course. I'd have liked to have recommended the beautiful, now stuck in my teeth, quinoa porridge but even I wouldn't give that to screaming Tarquin. No, instead ladies and gentlemen, behold mother nature's giver of life, the fruits of independence, the ladies lunchables, the baby buffet … the breast. And right on cue, out one flopped with no preamble.

On any other day, I would have ignored this perfectly normal behaviour but the unapologetic unveiling of the mothership, which was totally in my face, got my back up. Not usually one to cause a scene, I made what can only be described as a long lingering sigh that inferred someone had taken a shit in my lap, and swiftly said, 'I'm moving … ridiculous.'

And then it happened. 'Excuse me, I hope you're not tutting at me? Are you offended by nursing?' one of the mothers quickly fired at me.

'I love the birds and I love the bees, but it's nine in the morning, and I'm not ready to see boob,' I replied, knowing full well this was the kind of smart-arse comment that absolutely *wouldn't* diffuse the situation.

'What's your problem? I see you work at the gym upstairs. You're a great advertisement for them,' she quickly chirped back whilst trying to get support from her friend. Her reply was so sharp, that I thought this probably wasn't the first time she'd had to justify feeding her littlun from the teat of bourgeoisie. I could have left it there, but I was hangry AND annoyed that I had to move; plus, why wasn't it obvious what the issue was?

'You know what, I'll tell you what my problem is. You breastfeeding your child isn't the issue. The issue is that you took no notice of the other people here who might feel uncomfortable with what you're doing. There are literally, empty seats everywhere, and you chose to come and sit right next to me. There are ways to do this, and not to do this, and you chose the latter. In fact, I don't think you were oblivious at all, I think you did it on purpose.'

'What on earth do you mean? I'm allowed to do whatever I please, wherever I please, I have a child, for crying out loud,' she barks. #

Nope, nope, I'm not letting this go. 'No, you're not allowed to do whatever you please! You're in a public place with other people,' I replied.

Roll up, roll up, get your tickets to the 'Matt's not going to win this argument' show here! No price tag, it's a free-for-all. COME GET YOUR TICKETS!

'I'll do as I see fit, and if you don't like it, you can go somewhere else, can't you?' Her tone shifted from angry to condescending.

'I DID, I moved to another seat, but you got all pissy about it, so I can't win!'

'I DIDN'T get pissy, I asked you a question,' she said, determined to pursue the battle.

'If you don't like the answer then don't ask the question' I replied. At this point I noticed one of the coffee servers (who I might add was female) smirking. This is the WORST thing to do to me. I will ALWAYS rise to the occasion. I continued …

'You know what? You're just a little bit "Jehovah's Witnessey" if I'm honest. You know, you push it on people, you don't give them a choice. You could have been more discreet about it, given people are eating breakfast and there is plenty of room. You wanted to be in my face because we're in Planet Organic, and I'm male and I can't or won't say anything. I see you lot come in here every day,' I now include the whole of the local primary school mothering brigade into this – there are no bounds to my mistakes 'Sure, it's a safe place, but your ignorance to others is disappointing. I don't see you guys doing this in Nandos do I? Or maybe you do, I can see it now: "Yes madam, would your baby like the medium, hot, extra hot or lemon and herb sauce with their milk?" No, NO I DON'T.'

'You're so rude,' pipes up another mother.

'I'm not rude, I'm telling the truth. Madam if you'd ha…'

'Don't you DARE call me madam! Do NOT assume my gender!!' she shouted, cutting me off mid-sentence.

Oh, Jesus. I can't handle this anymore. 'Assume your gender? ASSUME YOUR GENDER?!?! I don't see any men around here breastfeeding their children, do you? That can only mean one thing, LADY, you're female!! Granted they gave men nipples, so we don't look weird naked, BUT I KNOW THE DIFFERENCE BETWEEN A MAN AND A WOMAN.' I can hear Stonewall banging their drums in the distance.

For context this all took place in 2016; in 2022, this sort of comment would probably get me sectioned or on the gallows alongside J.K. Rowling and Julie Burchill et al. It's a good job I've matured right?! Anyway, cue the human sacrifice that was about to happen. So much for being vegan, I thought. Weren't they meant to be against the slaughter of animals?

In came the manager, who politely tells me that I need to calm down and return upstairs.

I decline.

'Then I have no option, sir, but to ask you to leave.'

'Why, what have a I actually done? I sat somewhere else because I wasn't comfortable where I was, and you're going to penalise me for that? What if I'd have got up because they smelt like Gandhi's flip-flop? Would you have chucked me out then?'

'No, it's because you're an arrogant, white privileged male,' shouted an onlooker from the back, who I can only describe as ironically, a white privileged male. I turned to see what fuckknuckle came up with that one:

'Hey, pal, don't assume my gender!' I say, pointing the guy down at the back as he watches on. I'm in antagonistic mode now, knowing my efforts are futile. I'm going down fighting and I've now attracted an audience. Bring it on!

Lady to the manager: 'Why aren't you kicking him out and banning him from here, us women are all appalled!'

'Oh, so you're a woman now?' I nonchalantly say under my breath, whilst packing up my things.

'Oh, would you just shut up, man,' she replied.

'Don't you assume my gender either,' half laughing to myself. Game on.

'Pathetic.' She turned to the manager, whilst trying to rally her troops 'If you don't ban him from here, none of us will come back.'

'Why, where are you going to go? Nandos?' I am now in full Terminator wind up mode.

'WOULD YOU JUST…' She's totally lost it now. Baby clothes were being dropped all over the place, her canvas tote bag had fallen on the floor, and all its contents were littered under the tables. She even spilled coffee on her Balmoral pram. I kinda felt a little sorry for her.

'Look, OK, OK, I'm sorry if you felt offended, I guess it's true that breast is best, so let's just leave it. You don't need to go, I will.'

'ARE YOU STILL MOCKING ME, BOY?' she shouted as flames burst from every crevice of her being.

'No, I'm not mocking you. I've just now realised that I'm too privileged to have an opinion, and that if I did my sex would render it useless.'

'NEVER IN ALL MY LIFE …' She wasn't relenting, but sometimes you've just got to know when to exit the party.

Even though I'd somewhat instigated the whole thing, it reminded me of being kicked out of the classroom and summoned to the headmaster's office. I could feel the bullets being fired at me by everyone in the shop, hitting me so hard that they would make a trypophobic squirm at the size of the holes they left in me.

The barista was still smiling at me; a sly wink was shared across the counter. At least I knew I wasn't alone. That's one less bullet hole, I thought. Somehow, I made it upstairs to the gym safely. Even though I was now probably the number one target on mumsnet.com, I still had all my limbs intact. If anything, I was feeling somewhat more positive about the next session, so at least there was a silver lining.

What I haven't told you is that at one end of the gym, the whole wall was made from glass and looked directly over the seated area of the coffee shop. I'd noticed throughout my following session that the woman and the rest of the 'Witches of Wandsworth' had calmed down and decided to stay. Adamant on being crowned the breastfeeding winners of Britain's Got Talent, customers had unsurprisingly given them a wide birth.

Look, I knew I was in the wrong. Back then I was a gobby little shit who had a crowd spurring me to push it to the next level, and you could be forgiven for thinking that I'm anti-breastfeeding in public (and for the record I am categorically not) but there is a time and a place. Luckily for me, what happened next just proved that I was just another person in a long line at the end of their wrath.

With my last session done, I'd almost forgotten about the not so little incident downstairs … until I had to actually *go* downstairs. To leave the shop I had to go through the coffee area, which meant I'd have to come face to face with Voldemort and the Death Eaters again. As you can imagine – awkward. But what could I do? Leave through the back door? Be Spiderman and put on a mask, bend my wrist, cast a huge spider web and jump over the building? No, I knew I had to face it head on, because that's what you do, my warriors.

I walked down the stairs, spying the women who hadn't clocked me; they were already engaged in another altercation. I paused halfway to take in the scene, figuring out my escape plan whilst their attention had been diverted. Yes, yes, it was another dispute, and I'll give you one guess as to what it was about? But, instead of doing what any normal person would do in this situation and just leave unnoticed, I saw this as an opportunity to secure the last laugh. As I approached the all-female mud-wrestling match, the barista had me in her sights. Her grin almost resembled a Cheshire cat. I made my approach and gently moved in on the action, paying a small nod to the irate breast-feeder. Looking at me with horror, her victim turned around and saw me in front of her.

'I just wanted to give you a bit of advice' I said.

'Oh, what's that?' she asked.

'You want to watch out for this one,' pointing to the apoplectic Mrs Lactate with my thumb. I looked around, noticing that all eyes were now on me again. 'He's quite the feminist.'

All hell breaks loose.

VACATE THE ROOM

It was the latter end of 2016, and my time was nearing an end at the Planet Organic 'movement studio'. Danger was still working in North London and Irish was contemplating leaving the industry altogether, so I was starting to feel like I'd lost the camaraderie of the Three Amigos. My persiflage partner in Freddie had left for Indonesia, and now I was left alone with the tie-dye wearing knuckle draggers, in this newfound niche of the fitness and wellness industry that I'd found myself treading apple juice coloured water in.

I had been at the studio nearly a year, and the level of 'preachiness' had raised tenfold since my arrival. In that time, veganism had become king, bringing with it the next level of virtue signalling zealots. 'Health food' had gone into overdrive, with every single food on the planet having become sustainably sourced, eco-friendly, and, naturally, over-priced. Ridiculous new forms of yoga, including swinging your baby around your head, or sharing the mat with a goat or a dog, had become trends. Equally, the trainers and the yoga teachers who were now being employed at the studio had turned their self-righteousness up to notch eleven. There was a trainer who refused to be called by his actual name (he insisted everyone call him Coach B and nothing else), a

Pilates teacher who was so pro-life she assumed vegetables had feelings and a yoga teacher whose meditative sessions would focus on the healing powers of the vagina.

And ... then there was Amanda ...

Or, as she liked to be called – and this isn't a joke – 'Lucid Celestial Star Gazer'.

Lucid was an enigma to me. In fact, she was an enigma to everyone who worked there. Bear in mind that the majority of people who graced this studio were peace loving liberals and even they found Lucid hard to stomach. A complete personality oxymoron (moron being the operative word), she hailed from a very conservative family and was privately educated in one of the best boarding schools in the country. And yet, upon first looking at Lucid, you'd think she was born and bred in the Amazon by sun-worshipping witch doctors. But this isn't what confused people. Whilst she thought she was raised by Navajo dreamcatchers, her political agenda didn't match her somewhat capitalist Kim Kardashian-inspired ideals.

For instance, time and time again, Lucid would nag other trainers and her clients about the clothes they wore, or the way they made money (if they weren't ethically sourced, shame on you.). She used to relish preaching to anyone who would listen about how commercialism and consumerism was going to eventually kill the world. And yet here she was, dressed head-to-toe in haute couture leisurewear.

A hypocrite, yes. An eco-warrior, no.

But this was just the tip of the iceberg for Lucid.

This is where I will delve into the wellness pandemic I mentioned earlier. Mystical Holistical on overdrive.

For the purpose of this story, I'm going to call this company – Poop.

Poop was founded by the glitterati of Hollywood, whose understanding of health and fitness is questionable at the best of times. At worst, it is imbecilic and dangerous. Notions that spinach smoothies are going to 'heal' the body, women who lift over two kilograms are 'masculine', and ideas that those who do spin classes have big legs are all a precursor to poor information and a level of ignorance that gave birth to Poop. As I mentioned earlier, it's predominantly females who fall into the wellness trap (whereas men always fall into the bodybuilding trap) and how could you blame them?

Poop is now estimated to be worth more than $250million. It has its own series on a popular streaming service. It infiltrates women's glossy mags with its bullshit products and bullshit claims, hidden behind an air of 'doing right in the world'. The streaming service itself even distanced itself from the series' medical assertions, claiming the show is 'designed to entertain, not provide medical advice'.

This is not just an opinion that I hold, no. This is the opinion of many well-researched, knowledgeable scientists, who have debunked many of the claims Poop make for their products. NHS England Chief Executive Simon Stevens recently came out to say that Poop was a 'considerable health risk' to the public and accused it of spreading 'misinformation' with its 'dubious wellness products and dodgy procedures', and yet more and more consumers still buy into this company.

To give you a further idea of this shitshow of a brand, let me familiarise you with some of their products and/or health 'claims':

The Jade Egg Vagina Stone
Insecurity target:
Women who think, through poor education and media pressure, that their vaginas are not tight enough.
Claim:
The jade egg cleanses your reproductive organs and makes sex better, as it works like a Kegel stone which strengthens the vaginal wall. Kegel exercises are legit by the way.
Reality:
The stones are porous, meaning they are impossible to clean, which means you're probably going to have a long period of time using a cream for bacterial vaginosis.
Result:
Poop was sued and forced to pay a six-figure settlement, in a

class action brought by ten California District Attorney offices.

Sun Potion Mason Pine Pollen
Insecurity target:
Women, who are more than likely hitting menopause, think this lovely extortionately expensive bottle of bullshit is going to give them their sex drive back.
Claim:
Inspires the mind, balances hormones, enhances energy levels and builds immunity, whilst turning you into the female version of the Danger Toddler.
Reality:
You've just gone and wasted nearly 60 quid on a bunch of wild herbs.
Result:
This supplement isn't regulated by the FDA, so be-fucking-careful. There is also no evidence to back up any pine pollen sexual health benefits – surprise, surprise.

Vaginal Steaming
Insecurity target:
Women are told that they have the devil incarnate living in their uterus. Better steam that little fucker out of there like a Chinese Bao Bun roll.
Claim:
Steaming the vagina releases the toxins that are trapped in the uterus.
Reality:
If the uterus was so toxic how on earth do you think children are born?
Result:
Devils still walk the earth alongside a shit load of women with itchy inflamed treasure chests.

But that is not all.
I'm not just going to leave you with the three that stood out the most to me, because, in January 2021, Poop reached new

levels of tinfoil-hat crazy, when the famous owner launched her own line of candles that smelt like her own vagina. A 'funny, gorgeous, sexy and beautifully unexpected scent', a mix of 'geranium, citrusy bergamot, and cedar absolutes juxtaposed with damask rose and ambrette seed' ... thanks for clearing that up.

That's the next secret Santa present sorted.

Anyway, rant over. Let's get back to how this information is applicable in the story of Lucid Celestial Star Gazer.

Over the last two months of Lucid's pregnancy, she had become even more of a bore to everyone at the studio. There is only so much you can bear of unsolicited nonsense about natural pregnancies, home births and herbal healing. Add into the mix an unhealthy vitriol for anyone who didn't share her views, and it's fair to say that she had become quite unpopular.

Always one to champion the underdog and despite not liking her, I never let her eat alone and wouldn't leave when she entered the room. This allowed me more access than I probably would have liked, as I learnt that she was raising her child vegan and without religion. She was also looking into some self-healing postnatal techniques that included eating her own placenta. Despite the risks involved (and there are some very real risks if any of you out there are wanting to do the same), Lucid was adamant that eating her own placenta was going to bring her, and her new-born, back to Planet Earth's core.

Not one to be a prude, I was interested to know the details. Not unlike most self-righteous people, they will always give you an ear if you are interested in what they have to say. I wanted to know what it would look like. What it tasted like. How would you cook it – do you even cook it? How long do you keep it before you have to eat it? You know, essential details.

Lucid had all the answers, and it was therefore agreed that she would save the placenta for me after birth. She wasn't saving it because I wanted to eat it, for the record!

I had other plans.

It was around two weeks after Lucid had given birth to her little nipper, who I still didn't know the name of, but assumed it was Moonraker, or something equally ridiculous, when she came back to show everyone her latest prize possession. Whether you liked her or not, it was hard to ignore a proud new mum and her child. After the normal pleasantries, and cheek pinching and small talk, everyone now made their excuses and left the reception area. This suited me down to a T, because it now allowed Lucid and me to sit down together to discuss the birth.

We got straight down to business and entered into placenta talk. My heart was pounding, knowing I was about to witness some noxious god-awful sight in the name of human offal.

'Mandy, did you bring it with you,' I asked her, whispering under my hand even though there was no one around.

'Yes, yes, yes, I did,' she said excitedly. 'It's such a beautiful thing, it really is. Mother nature is so artistic in its form. Would you like to see it?' she asked, genuinely delighted she had someone who seemed interested.

Of course, I want to bloody see it. I used to stick my fingers in plug sockets as a kid, what do you take me for?

As she sidled over to her pram, she delved into the under carriage and pulled out what I can only describe as postal service parchment paper tied up with parcel string. She managed to get it on top of her lap, like a precious piece of gold leaf and then started to undo the string.

Boom-bada-boom, my heart was beating like a silver back in mating season. And then it hit me … The distinct smell of dried iron on flesh. Its bitterness riffled my nosc hairs making me gag. In front of me was what I can only describe as a large purple, veiny lily pad, with dried clotted spots of blood that hung to the purple veins like limpets on a boat's undercarriage.

'Whoa, enough, *enough*,' I spat, gently closing up the parchment so no one could get a look in. Whilst the smell wasn't as infiltrating as Freddie's urine, it wouldn't take long for someone to catch on that something may have died at reception.

Instead, my plan was about to kick into action.

'Mands, are you gonna eat that now?' I questioned innocently.

'I can do. Shall we share it?' she asked, not realising I wanted no part in eating the human carrion.

'No, no, I'm good. I just wanted to see what you thought of it. Intrigued, you know?' I said, trying to appease her interest.

'OK, sure,' she replied willingly.

Without any hesitation she pulled open the parchment and tentatively picked up the lump of half wet/half dried placenta and observed it from all angles with a grin on her face. 'Utterly fascinating,' she said, inspecting it like a new species.

At that very same point in time, Mr Horror walked back into the reception, totally unaware that Lucid was now tugging and pulling on her placenta *with her teeth*, like a lion on sinewy springbok.

My plan had been executed with perfect timing. We were about to get a meeting of the minds. Mr Horror vs another, actual horror.

It took all of about ten seconds for the aroma of blood to reach Mr Horror and a gaggle of other interested trainers.

'What is happening here?' Mr Horror shouted, now realising he'd stepped into a human safari.

The three other trainers stood by grimacing at the spectacle in front of them. Lucid —with blood either side of her mouth — looked at all four of them and offered them a bite.

At this point I lost my shit, and was snorting like a pig, laughing through my nose like a naughty schoolboy.

'Amanda, I'm going to have to ask you to leave. There is a time and a place, and this is not the time, nor the place,' Mr Horror affirmed, as he tried to usher her pram out the way of clients entering the reception area.

By now, there was a growing crowd. A crowd all stunned that Lucid had ignored all the requests and was carrying on devouring her former innards.

Lucid ignored Mr Horror.

'It's quite sweet, Matt, are you sure you don't want any?'

'I'm fine, my darling, you crack on,' I replied, still hurting from the internal laughter. There's one thing I'll give Lucid and that's her tenacity.

Mr Horror, knowing full well he wasn't getting anywhere, stormed out of reception closely followed by the disgusted punters and the other trainers.

Lucid, oblivious to everything, looked back at me like Hannibal Lecter on day release: 'What? What's just happened? What's wrong with people these days? This is the most natural thing a mother can do. It happens in the wild all the time. I mean, most mammals do this with their young. It's called placentophagy. Why do people have such an issue with it? If only they knew that mother earth moved in myster...'

She was on another one of her rants. I decided to interrupt it.

'Mands, I think you need to go and look at the mess you've made, girl. You look like Dracula,' I tell her, trying to break up the lecture I was about to endure.

At that point she realised it hadn't been the cleanest thing to eat and wrapped up the empty blood stained, reeking parchment paper, and put it into Mr Horror's waste paper bin.

Cue my second laughing fit of the day.

As I sat there looking after her sleeping babe whilst she cleaned up her face in the ladies, I felt rather philosophical on this little un's future. It was going to be an interesting little life this one was going to have, and then my train of thought was promptly interrupted by Lucid's return.

'Matt, can I ask you something?' she asked as she sat back down.

I could tell she wasn't quite with it. Maybe seeing herself in the mirror with a blood-soaked Joker smile hadn't helped.

'Why do people not like me here?' she asked.

Here was a woman who, I genuinely thought, couldn't give two fucks about anyone. Yes, she was highly annoying, yes, she was a bit of a contradiction, but underneath it all she was slightly clueless as to her effect on people. I don't want to end this chapter on a sad note, because it isn't. Lucid was a pain in the ass most of the time, and she actually wasn't very nice to people. She repelled more people with her rhetoric than she did by not wearing any deodorant. It wasn't rocket science.

'Mands, look, whilst you might think it OK to be super liberal, a lot of people aren't. You can't just act like it's your way or the highway. You need to b …'

She stopped me mid-sentence, not even wanting to hear the answer. '…But if only people would listen to me. I'm trying to change the world one person at a time, and if they don't like it, it's their problem. We aren't all enlightened, but we should try to be,' she said.

'Amanda, sorry to cut you short, I may have a solution,' I interrupted.

'Oh, what's that, Matt? Are you going to deny your private education and live a better life? Are you finally going to denounce your materialistic ways? Are you going to be a seeker in search for the ultimate goal? If only you'd change your ways child, and see the wor …'

Na. Off I toddled down to Planet Organic straight to the vitamins and minerals section. If I couldn't get her any lobotomy pills, I'd need to get the next best thing. Twenty-five, overpriced pounds later, I returned upstairs with a bottle of Ecological Formulas Placenta pills. 60 caps to be precise. I took the bottle out of the bag.

'I have a little idea for you…' I said, wondering if she'd understand the irony of the gesture. 'You might get more friends if you take these.'

Her face, unlike the cost of the pills, was priceless.

This incident happened long before the deadly Covid-19 Coronapocalypse virus hit the world, but as I write this during lockdown number two, summer 2020, I have observed something which should fully illustrate how silly the health and wellness sector has become.

To this day, I have not yet seen any crystal healers, homeopaths, naturopaths, Chinese herbal medicine practitioners come to the rescue with their 'all ailment' remedies, 'all saving' snake oil products.

That should tell its own story. Food for thought, don't you think?

PART SIX

THE WEIRD WORLD OF FAT LOSS

LESSON SIX:

There are no quick fixes to fat loss. No machine will get you there quicker unless it's chopping limbs off. Fat loss aids are not sex toys. And please remember that coffee should only go in via your mouth – not the other end.

D on't eat carbs in the morning. Don't eat carbs at night. Crikey, don't even eat carbs at all. Eat more protein. But don't have too much protein. Eat fruit. But fruit contains too much sugar. But be sure to get your five-a-day. Smoothies are good for you. But too much fruit will make you fat. Diet Coke will give you cancer. Carbonated drinks rot your teeth. Drink more water. But don't drink too much. Alcohol is the devil. Except Champagne. Good fats are good. Bad fats are bad. Eating fat makes you fat. Say no to margarine. Eat more butter. Eat less and move more. Intermittent fast for the best results. But eat breakfast like a king. Eat every two hours. Eat less red meat. But you have to eat more red meat for iron. Be more alkaline. Don't eat gluten. Don't eat lactose. Be cruelty-free. Eat 'grass-fed' only. Eat organic. Goji berries are super foods. No food is a super food. Milk contains pus, but drink more milk for calcium. Be kinder to cows – drink almond milk. Be kinder to the earth. Drink more soya. But avoid soya because it contains too much oestrogen. Eat dark chocolate, it contains antioxidants. But remember not to eat chocolate because there's too much sugar in it. Do more cardio, do cardio in the 'fat burning zone'. But remember cardio shreds muscle. Be more anabolic. But don't take supplements, you just need to take more vitamins.

Walk more.

Run.

Don't run.

Swim don't run.

Sleep, but not too much.

Eat, don't snack.

Except nuts.

But don't go nuts.

The list goes on and on. No wonder we are all fucking exhausted.

I was born in the early eighties, the first era of ridiculous personal fitness. I remember watching my mum knacker her knees doing step aerobics in the living room to a Jane Fonda VHS. I'm sure she had the neon sweatband and leg warmers too.

In the early nineties, bodybuilding peaked. All my action figures, G.I Joe, He-Man and WWF (now WWE) were all ripped with muscles. Even the third incarnation of my Teenage Mutant Ninja Turtles toys looked like they'd been on a course of Trenbolone. Yes, my formative years were spent learning that you can't be a hero without a load of bulging muscles.

One thing was clear: popular culture sensationalised the fitness world. And I became hooked. However, I didn't pay much attention to the fad diets; it was all about the aesthetics for me. Not too dissimilar to what is happening today, with celebrity-inspired six-packs and fake eyebrows. Looking back, though, I now realise that people were just as confused back then as they are today. The Grapefruit Diet, Cottage Cheese Diet, the Beverly Hills Diet, Elizabeth Taylor's Diet, the Scarsdale Die t …

I mean, we have to give ourselves top marks for trying. But what is truly fascinating is how none of these 'diets' survived. And that's the way it is with fat loss. There are so many ways to do it, but you'll always get someone who tries to package it up into a nice shiny little gift for you that makes it sound more important than it really is. The majority, if not all, are just based on the premise of calorie restriction. Hell, I could give you five new fat loss diets based on calorie restriction that I've just made up two seconds ago:

1. **The 1:4 Diet**

(You only eat one meal out of the four you were going to have that day – guess what? Calorie deficit.)

2. **The Air Diet**

(You eat nothing but air 24/7…Guess what? Calorie deficit). You might laugh but someone has actually tried to bottle air and sell it. I shit you not.)

3. **The Sleep Diet**

(You don't eat anything whilst you're asleep – duh!)

4. **The Cave Diet**

(You are only allowed to eat one thing per day, which is a fruit that's only found in the deepest darkest cave in outer Mongolia – which basically means you can't get it).

5.**The Death Diet**

(Follow the first four diets and you'll be dead within five weeks, so you don't need to worry about losing fat).

OK, so quick disclaimer. Please do NOT do any of the 'diets' above. It should be common sense, but, well, common sense seems to go out of the window when it comes to weight loss. Don't believe me – go speak to the people who think it fun to stick a funnel up their ass and pour a Starbucks soya latte into their rectum.

The world has gone mad.

Anyway, welcome to the weird and wonderful world of fat loss …

CABBAGE SOUP

The following story genuinely stopped me from working as a massage therapist ever again. In fact, it even went to the extreme of stopping me from massaging loved ones, that's how bad it was.

You have been warned.

Back when I passed my personal training qualifications, circa 2006, I had the opportunity to further my knowledge by training as a sports massage therapist. On top of the PT course, the therapy qualification took around another two months (60 per cent longer than most PT courses these days), and it was probably the most valuable thing I did. It helped me understand physiology and anatomy to a level most PTs ignore. I didn't undertake this course to be a therapist, per se, I used it as a platform to be a better PT. That said, there were often times when clients would ask for sports massage, and it soon became a successful bolt-on to the business.

I'd now completely left the heights, or the lows, depending on how you look at it, of the movement studio above Planet Organic. Whilst I had still kept a few sessions in North London going, I had let that end of my business slip and it was losing its feel of exclusivity, so I felt like I needed to change tack or start again. This is where I'd like to introduce you to my saviour at the time – Tammy.

Tammy was a middle-aged rock chick from some chi-chi part of LA who'd made it extraordinarily big in the finance world. After retiring in her early forties, she decided to set up camp in a multi-million pound house in the leafy suburb of St John's Wood, a stone's throw away from Abbey Road Studios and my old stomping ground – The Cave.

Tammy had contacted me through another high-profile client, who had mentioned that I was 'a lot more than just a personal trainer'.

Tammy wanted the works. Personal training four times a week, a massage twice a week, all her nutrition sorted, and all her meals pre-made and delivered. At the time, I was offering all four services, but I hadn't yet packaged it up in a nice tidy little marketing bundle that I could sell for a premium. But Tammy, not unlike many of her counterparts in LA, came with some very odd ideas about nutrition.

This successful woman was smart as hell, as quick as a whip, and you'd be foolish to think that she hadn't earnt her luxury dream house. But, she still thought that 'waist trainers' were the best way to lose fat, coffee enemas were the key to good digestion, and detoxing the liver with a juice cleanse every four weeks would miraculously stop cancer. And she thought the sun shone through the clean-smelling a-hole of the aforementioned Poop.

After a brief introduction through the mutual client, I set up a consultation on the phone to figure out what she wanted from me. After the call, I realised that I had my work cut out. I knew I was fighting misinformation and 'alternative truths' from La La Land, because while this woman had masterminded a small fortune, she was very much getting her health information from fake news.

We agreed to train at her house, and on my first visit I was amazed by how insane it was. By now I had spent the majority of my career in high net worth circles. I had travelled overseas with numerous clients in houses that you only ever see in movies. I had been on pimped out private planes, private yachts and been to summerhouses that were bigger than most people's roads. It's fair to say that I had seen the heights of what money can buy, and what taste can't buy you. Tammy, however, was different. Her house was utterly-butterly, a real sensation.

As I drove up the long drive towards the mansion, I was greeted by a building that I can only describe as a *Grand Design's* model home. Pillars of sand coloured concrete walls stood 40ft high blending effortlessly between large mahogany-coloured blocks of wood, which jutted out like carefully crafted carpentry. Long shards of glass were set perfectly in between the concreted masterpiece engulfing the interior with light from the heavens. As you entered the house, two large oak doors opened up into the lobby area to greet you. Freshly polished concrete floors gave the ground floor a minimalist industrial feel, whilst beautifully polished metal balustrades adorned the bespoke staircase that led to the first floor. Modern art littered every wall like an art gallery in situ. Carefully placed sculptures took you through the home effortlessly, whilst soft light came through the skylights bouncing off the sharp metal angles of the door handles. It was a peaceful haven of a house that had been executed tastefully. There wasn't a piece of gold or crystal anywhere to be seen.

And then there was the gym.

After a few pleasantries and a green tea in the minimalist kitchen, Tammy offered to take me through to where we would be working over the next few months. As we left through one wing of the house, I couldn't help but notice how nice everything smelt. On either side you could see into the garden area where the landscaping had been developed over three tiers of lush green grass, all filled with an array of white petalled flowers. Small Velux style opened windows in the walkway roof allowed a warm breeze to radiate the glass walls that I can only assume brought with it the fragrance of spring.

It didn't take long to get to the end of the hallway where we were greeted by another large door that Tammy unlocked. As she heaved the large door open, I was immediately struck by a wave of heated air and chlorine. Inside the room there was an indoor black tiled swimming pool, tranquilly glistening in the midday sun. The pool spanned the length of the room where it ended at a huge glass window that overlooked the rest of the garden, and the most amazing gym, sorry, home studio, I have ever seen in my entire career.

The studio itself had been built as a glass cube that attached itself to the poolroom. The swimming pool started indoors and with the flick of a switch, one half of the glass panel retracted upwards so that you could swim outside along the side of the glass cube gym. Next to the gym was a small therapy room that wouldn't look out of place in an exclusive five-star hotel.

It was this room that would be the end of my career as a massage therapist.

About four weeks into training Tammy, we were finding our feet and getting to grips with her new eating plan. Whilst she was open to my method, she couldn't help but constantly read the glossies and update me on her thoughts on new diets that seemed to spring up every week. Despite seeing her a whole lot more than any other client (five hours per week) I was still competing with the other 163 hours, which is where most clients go wrong. No matter what I did or said, Tammy would be on her own agenda with regards to nutrition. The pre-made meals I had arranged were fairly gross (this was before meal delivery services were as sophisticated as they are today), so it was obvious that she gave up the fight with those pretty quickly. I simply didn't have control over what was she was eating and drinking.

I thought I'd heard of the most ridiculous concoctions this industry could come up with regards to nutrition, but it wasn't until I met Tammy, that I realised I was merely knocking on the doors of the lunatic asylum. Over the next few weeks, I heard a cascade of strange methods of how she could lose weight, which led me to try to find ways of discouraging her. I shit you not, these included:

Drinking her own period blood.
Coffee enemas.
Fat freezing.
Cotton ball diet.

To name but a few.

Luckily, the brains behind a small fortune thought better of the four methods listed above. She didn't end up shitting a soya latte, she didn't end up coughing up a fur ball, and she definitely didn't lose her fat in the frozen aisle at Marks & Spencers.

Nope, what she did was way, *way* worse.

It was well into our seventh week together, and my regular visits to her home had become second nature. I would enter through the front door on my own (she would buzz me in), and I'd make my way down the glass corridor to the leisure compound passing the beautifully manicured garden, enjoying the sweet smells of the now early summer along the way.

As I entered the property and made my way towards the corridor, I couldn't help but notice a different aroma in the air. What was once the sweet-smelling candy-like flowers from outside, a somewhat noxious odour was now pervading the house like a kipper behind a radiator. I thought nothing more of it, until I had reached the therapy room where Tammy was waiting for one of her weekly massages.

'I apologise for the smell, Matt, we've been brewing up some cabbage soup. I heard it's a great way to detox the body, whilst giving you all the right nutrients for fat loss. I'll give you some before you go, make sure you remind me,' Tammy said nonchalantly.

'I'm OK, thanks, but what have I told you about things like this?' I asked her, knowing I now had to debunk yet another farcical fat loss aid.

Tammy looked at me and said nothing. Instead, she started to de-robe, which was my cue to leave the room so she could get ready.

I must have left the room for five minutes or so, before Tammy called me back in to start the massage.

Not unlike the first time I entered the pool room, a hot wave of air gushed out of the door and enveloped my body in what I can only describe as a mixture of foul rotten eggs mixed with the sickly-sweet smell of joss sticks. It was GBH for the nose. I felt like

I had been thrown into a Dutch oven headfirst. It was pungent to say the least.

But with most natural smells, unless it's actual excrement, it doesn't take long before you get used to it, or it dissipates, so I simply continued to set up for the massage. For those of you who are unfamiliar with how a proper massage therapist works, then let me tell you something that you should always remember: A massage therapist should always protect the modesty and personal privacy of the client. This is the priority. What this means in practice is two-fold:

1) The massage therapist should be accustomed to placing towels in appropriate areas to protect sensitive areas, as well as keeping you warm. Remember, you are naked, and they are touching you. You are vulnerable.

2) The massage therapist should massage in a way that is effective in reaching the communicated goal. In short, they shouldn't massage areas that don't need to be massaged.

Remember this, because you are about to hear the climax of this story where this massage therapist (yours truly) failed on one of those two things.

I was setting up just as I normally would, when Tammy told me she wanted the main focus of today's massage to be on her calves and her hamstrings. That's absolutely fine, no drama.

I get to work.

I must have been about fifteen minutes in on the first calf, when I noticed that the smell just wasn't going away. As wave after wave of fetid virulent cabbage filled gas wafted up my nose, I began to notice Tammy tense up and grip the massage couch. This is not uncommon by the way. Often when massages get painful, clients grip on to the couch like novice surfers. However, there was more going on here.

'Are you OK, T?' I asked, sensing something unusual within her.

Red-faced, she cocked her head around to face me and said,

'Would you mind just leaving for a second, I'm a little uncomfortable and need to move myself?'

'Of course,' I replied, hoping that a breath of fresh chlorine air in the pool room, would reinvigorate my nose canal.

As I left I heard a loud 'brrrrrrruuuaaaack' and then a long sigh afterwards, followed by the distinct sound of the spray of air freshener. It sounded like someone had stood on a large inflatable duck and then tried to blow it up again. I couldn't help but laugh knowing what had just happened.

As Tammy called me back into the room, I was still laughing to myself at the unmistakable smell of Hawaiian Breeze filling the air with notes of tropical mango, pineapple and peach with a hint of cabbage to boot. Tammy repositioned herself and in the process knocked the towels over that I had carefully set up, so I set about replacing them.

At this point Tammy started jabbering on as she always did. She had released the valve and was now much happier, so I got to work on her tight hamstrings.

However, I still needed to leave the room another two times when Tammy came clean that the cabbage soup she was making was upsetting her stomach, which is why she didn't really want her back and upper body massaged that day. After a few bits of back and forth banter, we got into a deep conversation about her husband's business and what their future plans were. I can't really remember too much of what we were talking about, but what I do know is that it made me lose my concentration and, unbeknown to me, the towel that I had replaced to cover her glutes (her butt) had slipped sidewards revealing more than she probably would have wanted. At this point, still in full conversation, I noticed that Tammy was gripping the couch again. I really didn't want to go back outside, so, like a woodworker planning a table, I applied a little bit more pressure to see if it was just muscular pain, or to see if she needed to conduct the anal acoustic band she was playing.

As I leant over the end of the couch, with both my oiled hands near the top of the hamstring, they slipped sideways, pulling one side of Tammy's glutes with them, revealing the entrance to mount doom, the Japanese war flag, the fudge-packed dookie shoot, the devil's onion ring.

Like a cat out of a drainpipe, and with a sound that I'm sure registered a solid nine on the Richter scale, I suddenly felt a large, warm blast of liquid shoot straight up my right arm, up onto my neck and onto the side of my face.

Yep, you guessed it – she had evacuated her bowels all over me.

I looked like Andy Dufresne from *The Shawshank Redemption*, you know, when he crawled to freedom through five-hundred yards of shit smelling foulness to escape prison.

Yeah, I was covered.

I stopped. My mouth wide open. I could feel the shit on my arms, my neck and on my face. I actually couldn't believe what just happened to me.

My mouth was agape. Horrified.I could feel it *in* my mouth! It smelt as bad it tasted.

Tammy jumped up from the couch completely naked, ignoring the soiled towels that lay sodden on the massage table. She looked at me in horror and rushed straight out the room with an embarrassed yelp.

I froze, not able to speak because I didn't want to close my mouth. The smell made me retch, and I wanted to puke but I also didn't want to contribute to the mess. I was now on my own looking like I'd just inseminated a cow, with a faecal trail from my wrist to my mouth.

So what would any normal person do?

What would you do?

After, what felt like half an hour of standing there dripping in someone else's excrement, I swivelled to the door, still not closing my mouth and made a dash for the pool fully clothed. I was like Usain Bolt on speed hurtling full throttle towards the pool. As soon as I was about to enter the dark glistening water I heard Tammy in the background.

'Stop, STOP!'

Her words travelled in slow motion.

But there was no stopping me. I was already mid-jump when I heard Tammy scream.

Sorry Tammy, but you shit on me. There is no way you're stopping this wrecking ball.

I dived into the pool. Sweet chlorine relief.

I stayed underwater and swam frantically back and forth hoping that the warm water would wash away Tammy's sins off my new Nikes. I took large mouthfuls of water and spat them back out to try and redirect my taste buds away from human shit. I scrubbed my arms so hard that they must have uncovered a temporary tattoo I had when I was six. As I swam on, I looked up to see the shimmering figure of Tammy standing over the pool shouting something indistinct.

OK, she might have sprayed me like Old Faithful, but maybe jumping in the pool was too much? I'd obviously grown a conscience in my old age. As I arrived at the other end of the pool I slowly came back to the surface, knowing that Tammy was highly unimpressed that I'd probably turned her swimming pool into a toilet.

After a tense five-second stare-off, her in shock and me looking like a drowned rat, I started to make my way out the pool in my now squeaking Nikes.

'What the HELL were you thinking?' she yelled. 'I'm going to have to get this pool cleaned now.'

Yeah, *I'm* the bad guy.

I looked around for a towel and a mirror and to see if all the remnants of Tammy's colon had been washed off. I ignored Tammy fawning over her immaculate floor tiles, checking for shit stains, when I remembered that all my stuff was still in the dirty protest massage room.

'Tammy, I'm sorry, but I need to get my stuff,' I said ignoring that she might well be the most embarrassed person on earth right now. Instead, she was more concerned about the pool, standing there in her white dressing gown, with her hands on her hips overseeing the catastrophe that lay in her wake.

Not turning to look at me, probably because she was bright red at this point, she just put one of her hands in the air like she was shooing me off.

'Please leave! I'll get your stuff to you.'

Oh. Shit.

Just when I thought that my business was going to take off again, I lose a vital client because of something they did. For the life of me I don't know how it was my fault that she projectile defecated on me like a Jackson Pollock painting. On second thoughts, it might have been the two grand damage I did to the pool (it needed complete draining and for the filters to be thoroughly cleaned).

I didn't hear from Tammy for a few days other than to receive my bag via courier. To be honest, it was rather pointless as I sacrificed everything in it with fire later that evening. I was not running the risk of any contamination molecules that may have been left on them. There'd be nothing worse than going to take out your meal prep of boiled chicken and broccoli the next day, to find a turdlette hanging off the corner.

I still hadn't received an apology for being used as a diaper that day, and, out of sheer stubbornness, I never apologised for jumping into the pool. I was still reeling, and anyway, you try driving home completely drenched from head to toe. It's not that easy.

A week later, when everything had dried off, Tammy called me to explain how much the pool had cost, and that we should both draw a line under it and move on. She never apologised. Clearly embarrassed by the situation, she didn't feel comfortable training any more and decided to 'seek new paths'. Fair enough.

While this was a blow to me financially, I understood and agreed that it was the best thing to do. This incident had given me full-blown sports massage PTSD and even the whiff of cabbage these days makes me throw up. But there's always a silver lining to every cloud of shit …

Firstly, that day made me turn my back on massages altogether, resulting in me employing a therapist to take over that side of the business. Secondly, being a PT means always learning and evolving so from then on, I'd learned to keep my mouth shut during sessions. But the biggest silver lining that I take away from this story, is to not ever turn my back on good nutrition. On that day, I, at least, got one of my five a day.

SLENDERBONE

'What the fookin' hell is this?' Irish shouted, holding up what I can only describe as a tentacled device with six pads and wires that led to some kind of digital control unit. 'Which one of yous is usin' dis piece of shite? Have ye not got any common sense?' he carried on, directing his words at the whole staff room.

I turned around from my laptop, noticing Irish's flabbergasted face.

'What is it pal?' I asked, genuinely not knowing why he was so irate.

'Diiiis fookin' ting, Matty. Some fookin' idjit is using what looks like a bloody waist trainer aren't they?' he replied.

There were five of us in the staff room at the time, all getting on with our own business when Irish came in like a bull in a china shop looking for a locker he could use. After the whole Tammy saga, I'd found a new studio to work from. It was more Central London based, so allowed easy access to my North London clientele. It was somewhere between 2016 and 2017 at a time where the fitness industry was rapidly changing. Big conglomerate 24hr budget gyms and heavily invested boutique group fitness spaces such as Barry's Bootcamp and 1Rebel were forcing privately-owned one-to-one studio spaces to rethink, or close down. The dedicated personal training studios were now few and far between, so some of my old colleagues were struggling to find somewhere they could work from. Luckily, I had found this place.

Within a month of starting, I had brought in Irish and Danger, later followed by the PT equivalent of Heinrich Himmler himself – Kane. The new studio was an impressive 5,000 square foot space that had weathered the storm of the new breed of gyms popping up. At its peak there were about forty-five personal trainers, ranging from your bulky, bearded cross-fitters, to your elitist Olympic lifters, to your OAP low impact trainers and, of course, the new breed – the Social Media Influencer Trainer, and of course the prawns. I'm proud to admit that it drew in an eclectic crowd.

At the time of Irish's outburst, I was sitting next to Danger and three other trainers who were just as intrigued as I was at what Irish had found. It turned out to be one of those EMS abdominal trainers.

For those that don't know what these are, EMS, or 'Electrical Muscle Stimulators' most often come in the form of stuck on pads, or in the most famous of brands, the Slendertone, a band that wraps around your waist sending small shockwaves into your abdominal muscles. They claim to help build strength in the abs and – drum roll, please! –they can spot reduce fat on the abs.

Insert faceplant emoji here.

The evidence on EMS is a grey area, fifty shades of it.

Often, these companies will hire fitness models, bodybuilders and athletes to trick you into thinking that they achieved their bodies from these vibrating belts. One particular brand hired soccer megastar Cristiano Ronaldo to promote their product. Ronaldo does about four hours of cardio a day, has the best nutritionists in the world and the best strength and conditioning coaches money can buy. He looks amazing. But yeah, sure, it's an electrical stimulation waist trainer that gets him those world-famous abs.

Whatever.

Anyway, after a full five minutes of tutting and hissing that

EMSs even exist in our industry, Irish still wanted to know who the owner of it was.

'Come on you lot. Oim losin' me patience. Who be da shit house who uses this piece a bull?'

Danger pipes up. 'Calm down Liam Neeson, no one's taken your daughter.'

Two of the other trainers flatly refuted the claims and turned back to their laptops. That now left me and another trainer, Aim.

'Irish, bro, who gives a monkey's, let's test it out,' I said, grabbing the electrical octopus.

'Matty, if dat is yours then you and I are done, horse,' he told me without an ounce of humour in his voice.

'As if it's mine, pal.'

Sure, I was curious about the EMS claims and the tech behind it. There are times in fitness where a new product comes along claiming utter bullshit but you have to try it out anyway to see what it feels like, so you can debunk it yourself.

In the words of the philosopher Shaggy – it wasn't me. But I was cooking up a way we could make this situation entertaining.

Aim, one of the trainers that had been hired, was being suspiciously quiet. She had a face and body that would make any woman reach for the ice cream in despair, but Aim wasn't really the type who'd need to use something like this.

However, Irish wasn't letting this go.

'What about you, girl?' Irish asked Aim. 'Is this loada bollocks yours, horse?'

Aim stayed silent. There was something not right, and you could palpate the tension.

I decided to rescue Aim for Irish's crosshairs – he was out for blood. So I chimed in with my cunning plan.

'I hereby nominate every one of us to try this out for a week each. Results get written on the board here. Who wants to go first? Neeson?'

Irish looked at me in disgust and turned back to foraging through the locker: 'Ye fookin' idjit, ye.'

The two trainers in the room agreed to take up the

challenge and volunteered to take the first two weeks. Danger also agreed and took the third week, I had the fourth week and Aim had the final week. She also insisted her boyfriend would take part. Let's just call him Meat.

These were the results:

Trainer One
No positive results
'Felt like I needed the toilet every minute.'

Trainer Two
No positive results
'Waste of time.'

Trainer Three –'Danger
No positive results
'This did not give me bigger biceps.'
(The idiot didn't put it on his abs, instead he thought he'd be clever and try it somewhere it's not meant to go. He wouldn't be the first one to do this…more about this later.)

Trainer Four – Me
Bugger all positive results
'I feel like I've been in the Milgram Shock experiment.'

Trainer Five – Aim
Positive results
'Felt tighter abs. Was contracting more through the core. Felt like I had a good abs workout. Noticed a slight decrease in waist size but nothing major.'

Trainer Six – Meat
Positive results
'Felt a burn every time I used it. Abs are swole. I'm no longer 'flat' in the morning.'
(Flat is a term gym rats use to describe the muscle feeling like its deflated; swole means swollen.)

With the results on the board, it was clearly obvious to us all who owned the ab belt.

Meat.

On looking back, I think we all knew who owned the waist trainer. It was somewhat obvious. PTing next to Meat and Aim was like standing next to two talking anal enemas. Boy, did they talk a lot of shit. I have never in my life witnessed two PTs go so hard into sales mode overdrive with their clients. If these guys were working in the eighties, then they'd be the double-glazing salesman and Tupperware party peddler managers of the month.

Not one to ever spout a load of bullshit to further his career, Danger took a liking to both of them, or should I say Aim. I'd often find him in the staff room chewing the couple's ears off about their waist trainers, and how much money they were making on the side. As you can imagine, this did not go down well with the third Amigo. Irish, with a now permanent sulky look on his face, was hanging around the edges trying not to associate himself with any of them. In his view you were guilty by association which meant that Danger was now on Irish's avoid list for the foreseeable.

But this was not Danger's agenda, no. Danger was more interested in Aim. It was an opportunity to worm his way in, like he did with my old socialite housemate.

'I've got no fucking interest in that shitty waist trainer, have I, Boods?!' declared Danger, deflated that he even needed to justify himself. 'I don't have a bucket list. I have a fuck it list. It's a mile long and Aim is at the top,' he went on, not realising that he was going up against Meat – a man mountain full of synthetic testosterone.

Irish, hidden in the corner, now realising that Danger had no intention of selling waist trainers to his clients, settled his inner quarrel and piped up, 'Yeh, I'd hit her too …With me car.'

Danger looked at me, I looked at Danger, we both looked at Irish. Hilarity has returned to normal. The Three Amigos were back in business, regardless of Irish's insensitive toilet humour. He didn't want to actually hit her, just for clarity.

Now, whether or not it was Danger's persistence in following Aim around like a lost puppy, or the fact that the majority of the trainers had turned their backs on the two snake oil salesmen, Aim had mysteriously upped and left the studio and gone her separate way, much to Danger's dislike. Her boyfriend on the other hand, or should I say now ex-boyfriend, was left reeling in the staff room giving us an explanation of what had happened.

His version of events was that she was to blame for the waist trainer debacle. Apparently, she would force him to plug all her incentivised products to his clients otherwise she threatened to leave him, in his own words, he was bullied into it and didn't have a choice. The victim card didn't wash with us. We knew there was more afoot. But, at the time, his account of the situation was the only evidence we had, because no one knew where Aim had disappeared to. Had he murdered her? Had he turned her into a pre-prepped meal? Had she lost so much weight with her ab toner that she'd in fact shrunk like a character in an Eighties Rick Moranis movie?

Well, I hate to rain on the fat loss brigade. She'd left for another studio. Why, we weren't exactly sure.

Until about a month later when one of the other female trainers called G came running into the staff room desperate to tell us all why Aim had not only left the facility, but also why she'd left Meat.

Too bad bitching doesn't burn calories, because G would have given Slendertone a run for their money.

'You guys areeeeeent going to beliiiiiiiiieve what I found out,' she excitedly announced. 'You're neveeerrr going to guess what happened to Aim and Meat?!' she carried on, enticing us in with the biggest smile I've ever witnessed.

'Get on wid it would ya missus. Tell us da craic,' Irish replied getting straight to the point.

The trainer then proceeded to tell us that Meat's versions of events weren't entirely accurate. In fact, they were so far from accurate, that she felt it was only right that the rest of us should know exactly why Aim had left.

Aim had left Meat because …

Wait for it …

He had tried to use the ab toner as a sex aid.

'A what now …? How? I mean…what?' I asked, not understanding how a bunch of electrical pulse pads could, in any way, be used as a sex toy. A mild torture device sure, but a sex aid?

Irish was now cracking up laughing, the other trainers in the room were just as baffled as me, and – surprise, surprise – Danger, hand on his chin, was contemplating how this was possible and why he didn't think of it first.

'Yes, yes, Aim told me that he was putting them on his Johnson. You know, to try and make it bigger. That sort of thing.'

'Oh, as if,' I said not believing the bullshit.

'No, I swear, that's exactly what she said to me,' the trainer replied innocently.

'Even if he did, why would she leave him for it?' I asked.

'He's putting electrodes on his cock, Matt, to make it stronger/bigger, whatever, you choose …' she fired back alluding to something I'm still not getting.

'Yeah and what? That still doesn't explain why she's left him, though?' I replied, trying to save face.

'You don't know much about women do you, Matt?' she retorted whilst raising her little finger in the air and wagging it like a small pig tail.

Now I get it. Harsh.

Alas, new vital information had now been leaked into the lion's den. An imminent human sacrifice was now about to be plotted. You cannot tell the Three Amigos things like this, without some form of daylight ribbery action.

Meat, the lying toad, was now fair game.

Aim on the other hand, went on to leave the PT industry altogether and fell into full social media mode setting up a nutrition business for female competitors, which gained hundreds of thousands of followers. I cannot be sure, but it wouldn't surprise me if she was still selling other fantastical 'life changing' products. What was sad about this was that females have forever been playing catch up with males in the fitness industry. Female trainers have had a hard time cutting through the bullshit that's associated with their sex; the tripe put out by popular media outlets, the idiotic fat loss tips to get rid of bingo wings, or how to attain the 'thigh gap', just to get the respect they deserve. Male trainers have not had to climb that same ladder. So, for someone who can influence thousands, to put out something that has no benefit other than to teach people to be lazy, I thought/we thought was a huge step back. However, Aim was not around anymore, so our attention had to be turned to Meat and his ironically, not so large … meat.

Now, we were all adults here. We may not have had the maturity expected of us, but we weren't going to go to town on the poor guy. What we could do however, was throw a load of banter at the lad when we were all together, which, by the way, took place in the staff room the following day.

'MEAT!' Danger shouted as the big guy entered the room.

'I've been wanting to talk to you, I need your advice on something,' he continued, wrapping his arm over Meat's boulder-like shoulders, guiding him to one of the chairs. 'Tell me, how small do you think you need to be before you decide that you need to get bigger?' he asked.

'Well, I don't know, it depends on …' Meat tried to answer the question before Irish cut him short.

'Horse, would ya agree that girls always say they appreciate the LITTLE tings in life?'

'Er, yeah, I guess, what's this all about?' he asked, fathoming that something is going on.

'Leave the man alone,' I said. 'Meat … do you put milk in your whey protein shakes? You know, 'cause milk makes your BONEs grow.'

'That's poppy*cock*,' one of the other trainers shouted in the background.

'Alright, alright … al-fucking-right fellas. ENOUGH! Who the fuck has been talking?' Meat shouted, bursting red from ear to ear, looking at all of us with an intense stare.

'Don't worry Horse. Everyone knows that the primary

function of boobs is to make fellas look stupid and de primary function of dumb feckin' fat loss tools is to make lasses look stupid. But, for the life of me, why in the name of Mary mudda of Jaysus did ye wanna put it on ye cock for?' Irish asked outright.

'I didn't alright, she's fucking lying. If it wasn't for her constantly pushing those stupid things …'

'Yeah, yeah,' Danger said cutting Meat short again. 'Put a *cock* in it, we don't believe ya.'

Meat was ready to explode. There's one thing you don't do, and that's rile up a 20-stone juice monkey. 'LISTEN FELLAS YOU'RE REALLY FUCKING PISSING ME OFF NOW. YOU BETTER SHUT THE FUCK UP OR I'M GONNA …'

'Woah, Meat, it's only banter mate,' I say trying to calm him down. By now the tension in the room was palpable.

'WELL, FUCKING LEAVE IT THEN! If I hear another fucking word from any of you lot, then I'm done here.'

Most of the trainers went back to their programs on their laptops trying to avoid the uncomfortable silence. Irish was now sitting admiring the room with a smirk on his face. Danger was still contemplating whether EMS would in fact help his sexual prowess. I, on the other hand, hate silences. Something needed to be said.

'Danger! What you got for lunch today?' I asked trying to break the tension.

'*CoCK au vin*,' he replies without missing a beat.

Meat looked up shocked that someone's even dared to challenge him. Irish's eyes widened, knowing it's about to go off.

'You better make sure it's been deboned,' another trainer quickly replied.

The whole staff room lost their shit.

You can only be young once, but you can be infantile forever, and we had *ABS … olutely* no control over our immaturity whatsoever.

CHAMPAGNE SUPER ROVERS

'They didn't get angry because I took my shirt off and got booked, they saw my physique and got jealous.'
Mario Balotelli

Music boomed and battered the inside of my head, as if it was a pair of shoes in a washing machine. Rainbow LEDs danced across the room illuminating the plush booths that sat beneath them. Giant bottles of vodka adorned with flickering sparklers hovered their way above the heads of the nightclub revellers whose eyes were all fixed on our position. Countless women, all dressed to the nines, jostled their way to get a photo over the shoulders of the burly doormen that stood guarding the VIP area.

It was 2017 and I was at one of the most popular nightclubs London had to offer, sipping gin and juice with some of the most well-known footballers in the UK. The Premiership had just finished, and I'd been invited by my client (a football agent) to join the players and staff of a team – which will remain nameless – on a night out to celebrate their season ending. In any normal situation I'd have made my excuses and not entertained the idea. I'd always find that if I was out anywhere there would be a 99.9 per cent chance I'd be thinking about going home and sleeping. However, this was an opportunity. A good opportunity that would lead to me getting my first big time professional athlete as a client.

I've had to do some terrible things in my life to get money, one of which was regularly waking up at 4:30am to train clients. This day was no different. To my horror, I was absolutely shut-eye spangled. Going out later that evening was about as appealing as a butthole salad with croutons, but I did what I needed to do, poured some dressing on it and sucked it up. I was going out big.

I'd always been intrigued as to the lifestyle of footballers. Was what we see in the media really ever true? Well, I can tell you just from this evening that the lifestyle is somewhat true. They say they're trying to make Viagra for women but, by the looks of this lot in this club, all you need is cash, a Golden Boot and bottles of Cristal. The number of women who were desperate for a look in with the players was insane. Some of the team were shy, some were keeping it moderate (given that half the directors and management were here), there were the rowdy few … and then there was the one. The gobshite. The twat who had a booth to himself where girls were falling all over just to get in. This made his head so big you wouldn't have been able to fit a sombrero on the fella.

If you're picturing him now, imagine slicked-back hair, white shirt open down to his navel, ripped abs, gold Rolex, suede shoes with no socks. The piece de resistance, however, were the God-awful ripped skinny white jeans. The geezer looked like basmati rice.

Anyway, this guy was full of himself; shouting at the doormen, ripping a new one out of his teammates and being a general tit. It wasn't going to be long before something kicked off, you could feel it in the air, the atmosphere was palpable. And remember, I have a third eye about this stuff.

What I didn't realise, though, was that it would be me who would instigate things.

I'd been watching this top-flight player be a top-flight twat for most of the night. He was a ticking time bomb waiting to go off. I didn't like him, I didn't like what he stood for, but, ultimately, I didn't like the way he was treating the people around him. Including girls. It wasn't long before one of the girls was crying and that was it for me. I turned to my client, the football agent, who was ready to leave.

'Just leave it, Matt, he's not normally like this, it's the end of the season. He's just blowing off steam,' said my client.

'Don't make excuses for nasty people, John. You can't put a flower in an arsehole and call it a vase,' I fired back, knowing that I'm going to have to say something. What happened next is how I managed to obtain my first professional footballer client. I took the short walk over to his booth.

'You might want to apologise to that girl, pal,' I said, knowing he probably wasn't going to turn over a new leaf and apologise profusely. It felt like the whole club was looking at me. I swear I heard a record scratch too, and the music come to a grinding halt.

'Who the fuck are you? Fuck off, ya mug!' came the bleary-eyed response.

I scanned my surroundings. The doormen were uninterested in pacifying the player, so it looked like it was on me. He was spoiling for a confrontation but at the time I was 110kg and I'm 6ft 2in too – this scrawny little boob didn't stand a chance. Instead of raising hell, I told two of the girls to move from his booth so I could sit next to him. I leant into his ear while he looked at me with shock and told him that in this club he might be 'Billy Bigballs', but as soon as we stepped outside on the streets we were equals, and he better be able to back himself. For the life of me I don't know why I did this, maybe it was the four triple vodka Red Bullshits I'd had, because I felt like I had wings. To my astonishment, this calm but precise 'leveller' seemed to take the wind out of his sails. After I stood up, I watched him not only apologise to the girl he had upset, but, five minutes later, he came over to me – and started talking to me calmly and friendly. After a brief get-to-know-you chat, he invited me to the training ground the following week to assist in a hamstring problem he had. I'd got his respect. I was in.

For the next couple of months, I ended up assisting on some of his pre-season training and we grew quite close, to the point where he offered to let me drive any of his cars, which included his one-off Lamborghini. The person I stared down at that club that night was a completely different character to the one I got to know.

So, what has this chapter got to do with the weird world of fat loss you might be asking?

Well, in the short space of time of knowing and training this particular player, I came to realise just how much pro-footballers get inundated with sponsorship deals, especially when you were in as good shape as he was. In one week alone his agent (my original client) had sat him down in meetings with a peanut butter company, a health food company, countless supplement companies, multiple clothing start-ups and the one that topped it all off – a CBD company claiming huge weight loss benefits, which they wanted him to attribute his physique to. And, to his credit, he told me he turned them all down. On a surface level, this player presented himself like he would chew the arm off a BooHooMan deal, but the reality was he was far more considered about his image, his brand.

'Why would I take any of those deals, Matty?' he said when the subject came up during a session. 'I'm a professional football player, mate, I didn't get in shape with fucking peanut butter, did I?'

Not only was this completely against the presumed stereotype of the modern footballer, but he was now talking my language. The reality was that the amount of exercise this player did on a daily basis churned up the 4,000 calories he was consuming a day. Energy in versus energy out = calorie deficit = fat/weight loss. It wasn't rocket science, and it certainly wasn't peanut butter or CBD.

As I've spent the previous two chapters explaining to you about incidents that highlight how absurd the weight/fat loss industry can be, I wanted to highlight a cracking example of a public figure who didn't succumb to marketing ridiculous fat loss aides to his millions of followers and fans. He was looking at the long-term implications this might have on his career, his brand, and the implications it had on people who looked up to him. He wasn't thinking of the next pic on the 'Gram, or what his management company were trying to make coin from. He worked damn hard to get the physique he had; there were no shortcuts, no miracles, and no magic ointment that tasted like a grass ashtray.

You might be thinking that he would have taken these contracts if he wasn't making as much money as he did. But, let me tell you, regardless of all the cars and the houses he owned, he still had hard principles and realistic health goals. He wanted to win the Champions League, which meant he'd treat himself to his favourite car of all time – an Aston Martin (bear in mind he could have bought two of these a week already). He rarely drank (the nightclub incident really was a one-off); he looked after his diet religiously, and every week I'd set a fitness goal that he'd almost always achieve. And talking of goals, as we are about to enter the next chapter on social media psychosis, it's safe to say this footballer scored on and off the pitch.

#Squadgoals

PART SEVEN
SOCIAL PSYCHOSIS

LESSON SEVEN:

If you have to airbrush your physique then you're doing something wrong. Social media photo filters are the modern-day balaclava. If you go missing, everyone's going to be looking for Angelina Jolie, when really they should be looking for a bulldog chewing a wasp.

I n my twenties I ruled the world. Or, at least, I thought I did. I had my own studio before I was 30 and life as a PT was great. I had built a fantastic reputation in exclusive circles, and I picked up the business mainly through word-of-mouth. When client numbers were low, I'd run an advert in high-end local magazines, distribute flyers in the wealthier London suburbs and offer a new and enticing package to some of my more discerning clients, all of which worked.

And then came social media.

Or, more accurately, Instagram and YouTube.

Social media had been around for a few years, but I'd not paid much attention to it. Things were going well with the business, and I had no time to be posting pictures of myself in the studio. After all, social media was for kids, right?

Wrong.

I was about to learn a very important lesson with regards to online marketing.

It wasn't until I got myself back in the big time with my Central and North London clients in 2017 that I returned to my old South London territory. I had kept in contact with a lot of the rowers I had worked with and the majority of the Planet Organic soya matcha latte crew. It was now heading into the summer and people wanted to start training outdoors again, so I had the idea to run an outdoor bootcamp three times a week on Wandsworth common, one of the last parks that you didn't need to pay rent on (at this point the UK government had brought in a Park Tax for PTs just so they could stick another knife into the side of struggling personal trainers.)

So, how do you differentiate your bootcamps from every other Barry Bloggs in the park? Well, I invested in lots of cool equipment, bought branded flags (I named my classes Superhero Bootcamps) and made the sessions interactive. Over the course of three weeks, I had gone from pulling in five people to training around twenty per session, three times a week. This was all through simple, traditional marketing. Nothing clever, nothing fancy, but it worked. Dog walkers and mums-with-prams stopped to watch the bootcamps, and on the odd occasion you could see people taking videos and jotting down the web address from the banners.

However, outdoor bootcamps rely on good weather and the UK weather is about as unpredictable as a wasp on speed. It wasn't long before the rain came, and the bootcamp client numbers dwindled.

Along the course of running my bootcamps, I'd noticed another PT trying to do the same but struggling to attract new business. I'd often see him looking deflated with two or three clients and I felt sorry for him. He was a relatively young PT, good-looking and in great shape so I scrubbed it down to him just starting out in the industry. He would soon find his feet.

However, little did I know then, not only would he find his feet, he'd soon be able to buy boots of gold.

Nearing the end of the summer, as the English weather turned smiles into frowns, I noticed that my friend was pulling in the crowds. Not only was he attracting more clients than I was (with little to no equipment), but some of the people who were attending were high-profile TV and media faces.

What the hell was he was doing right? I had to find out.

After a quick introduction, and the usual roundabout way of trying to figure each other out, he revealed that most of his clients were coming through Instagram.

'Instagram, pah! I don't need that, isn't that for the selfie generation?' I naively barked to him.

'You need to get with the program, old timer. Your days are numbered if you think like that,' he said.

In any normal situation, I'd have slapped him so hard his grandkids would have had black eyes, but I also knew he was right. If he could transform his business in the space of just a few weeks without any of the traditional methods of marketing then I needed to know what he was doing and be even better at it. Unfortunately, with the sun lowering earlier, it was too late for my bootcamps and they died out with the hot summer evenings.

It wasn't long after I shut down the bootcamps that I started to see his face appearing in all the papers, lifestyle and health magazines and daytime TV shows. Just like that, in the space of a year – zero to hero. Boom.

Soon, he became one of the most successful social media personal trainers in the country. I'd been in the game for longer than half his life, and I wasn't getting anywhere near the amount of the recognition he was. I was more qualified, I had more experience, and I'm sure I'd spent ten times the cash he had on traditional methods of marketing.

And that was partly my issue. It meant nothing because I hadn't evolved. Instagram, Twitter, YouTube and Facebook advertising and marketing were now the key to publicity within the fitness industry and I was lagging behind.

But catching up wasn't just the only issue I was facing. I am a stickler for comparing myself to others. It's the trait of mine that I immensely dislike because it can only ever lead to insecurity. This is why I have an innate dislike for any forms of social media, and why I was so resistant to it when it first came out. Everyone wants to be better than everyone else, even if it just looks that way, and it's not the reality. But this younger version with much more success was a trigger for me. It made me insecure, angry, bitter, jealous and frustrated.

But it also made me wake up.

It was my time to adapt. I went into full social media mode.

And guess what? I hated it. I hated every fucking second of it.

Filming myself exercising in a vain attempt to become more relevant became long and laborious. Especially when it took me away from training actual clients. I started filming client lifts, but this not only pissed the client off, but also went against everything I stood for – privacy, exclusivity, professionalism. In an attempt to evolve, it seemed I had forgotten why my business was successful in the first place.

I quickly abandoned everything I knew worked and adopted this new type of millennial marketing. But instead of gaining clients, I ended up pissing off my existing ones. And as if it wasn't already going badly enough, to top it all off, I ended up herniating a third disc in my lower back trying to attempt a hard calisthenics move just for my social channels.

If ever there was a message from the gods about my actions, then it was this, because the resulting pain changed the way I worked forever.

I'd always found it fascinating how so many people, especially PTs, found the time to constantly update their Insta stories and keep a running commentary of their lives. I can't help but feel that these same people either never had many clients to begin with, or just don't have much going on at work.

I worked with clients every day; there was no time to constantly update my followers with stories, filming workouts and then editing them. Especially if I wanted them to look good. It was just not sustainable. And it certainly didn't make me a better personal trainer. And that's the whole point to all this, right? To *be* as good as possible. Not to *look* as good as possible?

I started to resent myself and the way the industry was heading. Anyone with a decent iPhone who was into fitness started doing the same thing. All of a sudden, everyone was a PT. These amateurs had followers increasing by thousands a day, whereas mine were going up about three or four, if I was lucky. So, suffice to say, not only was it killing my business, but I was also shit at it.

Was I too old?

Was I not bulging with enough muscle?

Was experience, qualification and integrity not enough? I truly didn't know anymore.

And, this is where the lightbulb moment pinged above my head. Instead of rising to this strained challenge, I changed my thinking.

What was it that made my business successful in the first place?

What did my clients want from me?

What was it that made people buy into my service?

What was my unique selling point?

And did that have a place on Instagram?

The answer was…

NO.

I was servicing the super luxury high-end of the market, not the paunchy middle. My clients were rich and the famous. They weren't buying off some beefed-up jerky on Instagram, who filmed themselves doing burpees with their top off. They valued privacy, secrecy, and a person who wasn't interested in self-promotion, because they were the centrepieces, not their trainer. These were clients whose average age was in their late forties. Did these people even use Instagram? Did they care about how good I looked posing in a stretched position on Hampstead Heath just so I could #lifegoals #lovelife #gymlife #ripped #fitnessmotivation #fitfam #lifestyle #instagood #instafit #abs #etc.

#Fuck #off.

My clients didn't care about any of that, not really.

However, I'd lost sight of who and what my clients bought into, and this is where so many people who use social media to market their businesses go wrong. Social media is not the be all and end all. And, post-pandemic, the rising of the cost of living, Brexit, and the unscrupulous behaviour of these tech giants in global elections, and so on, social media has lost much of its appeal to even its most dedicated disciples.

With social media, the number of likes is what you count, but the quality of your customer service is what you can count on, and the quality of your service will be around for as long as you pay attention to it. Regardless of how many likes you get.

Thankfully, I can now look at it objectively. I see it for what it is.

In the early days – it began at the same time as my career in PT; we've grown up together – it was an incredible tool for individuals and businesses to reach a much larger audience. Many people, like my Bootcamp friend, made big bucks out of it, and to be fair, in some cases, it still does that.

However, it's also grown into this wild beast that is changing perceptions in a grotesque way and is now rife within the health and fitness arena. It gave birth to the selfie generation. It facilitated unqualified Z-listers. It spread lies and hate about body health and fake fitness news. It allowed people with no fitness experience or qualifications to create a platform to sell ignorance to the ignorant. It told us that if you don't look ripped and tanned you were out of shape and undesirable. It allowed people to lie about how perfect their lives were as long as you hash tagged 'living your best life'. It taught the young and impressionable that if you weren't making enough money, you weren't successful. It taught us that 'likes' and 'followers' were a form of currency. It made girls get their butts, lips, boobs, ears, cheeks and noses 'fixed' where personal appearance meant everything. It taught us what its version of perfection is and then told us that we aren't perfect. We've learnt to fear rejection, to crave attention and affection and to dream of an unrealistic expectation.

However, there is a shift in tide approaching. As I write this, Facebook/Instagram have changed their algorithms and tried to do away with serial hashtaggers, those who bought their followers, or those that sell bad shit to good people.

Am I down with this? Hell, yes, I am.

I'm starting to see what I would call 'real' influencers fighting back. People with solid knowledge who actually educate people in a sensible way. *This* is what social media should be used for.

Unfortunately, I think the damage has already been done. Social media has left a huge skidmark on society and people now have even worse mental health issues because of it. We've become a culture judging ourselves only by what others are doing. And they're just as lost as the rest of us. We've lost the essence of our own purpose in this world because social media has us believe that those who are rich and famous and beautiful are unlike us. Well, that's bullshit.

Remember – pobody's nerfect.

PINKY & PERKY

*'Wouldn't it be great if we lived in a world where insecurity
and desperation made us more attractive?'*
Albert Brooks, *Broadcast News, 1987*

I have come face to face with a multitude of social media 'stars' over the years. From those who rent Ferraris for a day and tell people they own them (and, worse, act like it), to those that sell more drugs than their dealer and those who have the audacity to hashtag 'hustle' and 'work hard' when they grew up either beyond privileged, or simply had the right luck at the right time. There are those who live at home in their middle class houses, who take pictures of other people's pools and holidays, and there are those that use the liquefy filter on Photoshop to suck in their waist, so no one realises that the skinny teas they're hawking are a bunch of sweatshop shite.

And then there is Pinky, whose rise to social media fitness stardom has some horrible truths to it.

But before I carry on, I'd like to add a disclaimer here. While I may say things that come across as a little harsh in this chapter, I do not mean this to be a personal attack on the character who I am calling Pinky. Instead, this is an attack on the social psychosis that made her behave how she behaved. Hopefully, by the end of this chapter you will understand that I only use her story to further illustrate my point about the dangers of fitness industry social media, and how easy it is for the public to be fooled by fitness 'influencers'. Her story is a sad realisation of what is now prevalent in the current online social media fitness industry. It's a story about how people are being tricked by an image of perfection when the reality is so far removed from the truth. A story that, underneath all the glittery filters, the makeup and the surgery, is about a person who is deeply troubled.

But, let it be known now, Pinky's story is, sadly, anything but unique. Her story, not unlike many others, is happening time and time again under our very noses. In this particular case I was party to a lot of the home truths, which you need to know about so you can get a better idea as to the kind of bullshit that masquerades itself in gym wear. Because these vampires are after your money, plain and simple.

Let me begin by casting you back to when I worked at The Cave for the first time.

I was nearing the end of my time at the studio when Pinky first came on to the scene. It wasn't unusual to have fellow PTs drop in to view the place and enquire about rates to see if The Cave could work for them. Most of the time they'd take one look and make a run for it, knowing that they were entering into a fresh hell of damp sweat and leaking ceilings. But this one time, an out of shape 20-year-old female had managed to overcome the rancid smell of mould. She'd run the gauntlet of Danger and Irish and had jumped over the puddles of piss just so she could talk to me about something she clearly knew nothing about. I figured that if she managed to get that far, then she deserved my attention.

Pinky was a fresh faced, round girl from outside the city. At 5ft 7in she wasn't just curvy, she was clinically overweight – you could pinch more than an inch everywhere. Unfortunately, I sound like a prick even writing this; she wasn't really a looker either, with a set of gnashers that looked like she could chew an apple through a tennis racket. But bear with me, years later this would be a *very different* story altogether. She had come to The Cave because she wanted to know what it took to become a personal trainer.

My heart bled for her. Standing there in front of me was a girl who was trying to change the pack of cards she'd been dealt, and who thought that the best way to boost her self-esteem was to throw herself into the lion's den of the fitness industry in some vain belief that the validation from others would validate her. We all get into the industries we are in for different reasons, but the fitness industry is fickle, and no one, least of all me, wanted to tell this poor girl that it would be very difficult for her to pick up clients, given that she looked unhealthy and didn't even train herself.

So, over the course of about four weeks, I decided to help her out and show her the ropes of some basic workout routines. I taught her what a barbell was, what squats were and showed her enough so she could enrol on a personal training course, and not look like a complete amateur.

She qualified as a PT three months later.

She returned to The Cave in the hope that she might pick up a client or two. She had dropped a dress size. It was a start at least. Unfortunately, it was a slow road, and in my last few weeks at The Cave she only managed to get one client – the nail beautician next-door who was trading her nail treatments for sessions. Her early days as a PT were miserable and I felt for her.

Fast forward four years.

I'm back training at in the central London gym. And who do you think came through the door looking for work?

Pinky, of course.

However, this time it was Pinky version 2.0.

It was one of the most unbelievable transformations I have ever witnessed as a personal trainer. This girl was now unrecognisable, with lips the size of rubber rings, boobs that would make Katie Price blush, a booty that would be on the main menu at any celebrity LA nip/tuck clinic, and the emboldened swagger of a *Love Island* winner. Her teeth no longer looked like a burnt fence, and instead looked like she'd bought them out of a *Thunderbirds* gift shop. Pinky was so fake she made China's knock-off shops worried.

Over the course of the next few weeks, all the male trainers couldn't help but stare in awe at Pinky. Needless to say, Danger was in on the action. Irish and I, however, were baffled as to where the humble Pinky had disappeared to.

Naturally, my curiosity was killing me, so I sent Sherlock Hodges to detect the hell out of this little dichotomy. My first port of call was to have a little needle around the haystacks on the Internet and her social media. I trawled Facebook, Instagram and Twitter, which all proved dead ends. Nothing. Nada. Not even a LinkedIn account.

However, that all changed when I managed to get Pinky on her own and it took all of 3.02 seconds to figure out that she had, in fact, turned into a bit of a douche canoe. I say that because it had only been a few years since I last saw her, but in that time not only had she filled her body full of Botox, silicone and veneers, she'd also undergone a full frontal lobotomy as well.

She now had no recollection of who I was, despite me telling her that we'd already met before. She had no apparent recollection of The Cave, or ever having spent time with us being taught the basics of training. She either genuinely couldn't remember who we were, or she was in complete denial about her previous life. I say previous life, because she was now going under a different name altogether. Hence why I couldn't find her online.

It was time to do another social media search but this time with her new name.

Back in my day, people used to take pictures of themselves with other people in them, but clearly this was no longer the case. Thousands of selfies later, I was exhausted. It didn't take me long before I found out that Pinky – or Perky, as I shall call her from now on – was a new rising star on the social media scene, plugging glitter pills to make your faeces sparkly (yes, they exist!), and pushing pyramid scheme beauty products to her loyal followers. Vacuous, self-indulgent pictures of half hitched up thighs, one foot on a tip toe giving prominence to her paid-for bulging *glute medius*, and filtered snapshots of her bronzed abs, all adorned her Instagram wall. She had been posting new pictures almost every hour of every day for the last year, and had amassed over 100,000 followers, who, upon careful scrutiny, looked as though half had been bought. Her profile, at the time, claimed that she was a model, a PT, an entrepreneur, a 'model' and a 'bad ass boss bitch', but she also wanted people to know that she was still 'grounded'.

Sigh.

What happened to the Pinky I remembered with the uncombed hair, a penchant for doughnuts and wonky, jagged horse teeth?

I needed to know more, I wanted to know more. So, what do you do when you need to break the ice with a 'new' colleague? Arrange a social, of course. There's nothing that gets to the truth quicker than the happy hour juice, so off to the pub we went. Like the Pied Piper of Hamlin, Perky led the procession of all the male trainers, and revelled in the fact that everyone wanted to sit with her. She'd not only captivated all of the PTs' attention, but she was now holding court to all the other men in the bar like some kind of sex vuvuzela, while sporadically taking selfies and flicking her own hair as if she was in a Timotei advert – I'm showing my age here, aren't I?

I found it odd that she didn't remember me.

Something was up.

It was time to call in Danger. He'd been salivating over Perky all night and was not bothered by her transformation – he just wanted to bag whoever she was now, though he was curious to see what she looked like naked. Danger needed precisely zero convincing and did what Danger does in these situations and ignored everything around him. Off he went – in for the kill.

My plan to get to know the real Pinky had failed. Old Pinky was dead. Long live Perky.

It was all down to Danger to see if he could coax anymore information from her.

I left to go home.

Two hours later, at around midnight, I received a phone call from Danger.

We were about to learn a little bit more about the new version of Pinky.

'Boods, you're not going to believe this son,' he said exasperated. 'She's only a fucking brass, isn't she?'

'You what?' I asked, not believing what I'd just heard.

'Geeza, I went back to hers, had a couple more drinks and then she completely changed. Started saying that if I wanted anything more then I needed to pay her. I mean FUCKING PAY HER!'

I literally couldn't believe what I was hearing.

'Hold up, hold up. Did you pay her?' I ask, trying to make light of the situation.

'You're havin' a bubble, ain't ya? No chance. I wouldn't pay for that shit, na na na, especially not with her. She's so fuckin' borin' anyway mate, like a sleeping pill in a tracksuit. Na, man, wouldn't pay for that, never. Not me son. Noooooo way.'

As Queen Gertrude in *Hamlet* once said, 'The lady doth protest too much.' In this case, Danger was the lady.

He clearly had paid her.

Danger's revelation all became clear over the following few days.

Perky was pulling in the same type of client time and time again. Swathes of old, rich men who were clearly all clients of SugarDaddys.com came in and out of the studio to be 'trained' by her. They would shower her with gifts, drive her to and from her sessions in their latest super cars, or take her out to the latest mega-restaurant in Dubai. Now I knew, it soon became obvious to everyone around what she was doing. Then it all started to unravel.

Unfortunately, female trainers are the minority in the fitness world, and I feel for their struggles. Not only do they have to put up with a large amount of competition, but they also have to struggle with the media pressure of constantly staying in shape. As well as put up with a lot of alpha male, or seedy male, bullshit. A man can get away with being bulky and muscly and carry on PTing without a worry, but if a female trainer was to do the same then she probably wouldn't get much business, and she'd be more than likely vilified by other females in the industry. Female trainers, as I have learned, have to be Goldilocks – not too bulky, not too wiry. Just right.

I don't know if Perky was feeling the same pressure, or if she was doing all this just to further her social media career, but I do know that she had pulled on a couple of the other trainers' knowledge to help her get 'competition ready' for a bikini show later that year. One of the trainers who she'd picked out was a good friend of mine and was a well-established body transformation coach, who had countless examples of clients who had gone on stage. The other trainer, a he-who-shall-not-be-named kind of type, was what I would call … unscrupulous.

Within the first eight weeks of working with Perky, my friend had sacked her and the erroneous trainer had taken over in his wake. Here are the reasons why my good friend sacked her, followed by what actually happened:

Reasons
1)   She wasn't sticking to any of her diet. She was overeating and moaning that he wasn't doing his job properly.
2)   She was taking supplements that weren't prescribed.
3)   She started talking about short cuts. She was lazy and not training properly.
4)   She wanted maximum results with minimum effort.

What actually ended up happening
1)   She ended up having Ab sculpting liposuction. No joke.
2)   She started taking Clenbuterol and a thyroid manipulator (both illegal and non-natural).
3)   She got both points 3 & 4 from the above list.
4)   She ended up shagging the crooked trainer. Whether he paid or not is a different matter altogether.

Of course, she ended up placing in the top three at the 'natural' show and then, in true Perky style, she promoted the hell out of it. Her Instagram following went up by another 10,000 gullible followers in the space of a week.

And here is the fundamental lesson of this chapter. We all want to be impressed by something, or someone. We love to see lives that we would like for ourselves. We immerse ourselves in alternative worlds that fascinate us. The work of a beautiful artist, a woodworker or a sculptor is a sight to behold. To look at those who bring us incredible music, or others who create beautiful things that we only wish we could create ourselves, is a form of healthy escapism. But there is a dark underworld where a lot of us are being taken for a ride. In Perky's case, she is a victim of the things she peddles herself. Her social psychosis took over her life but underneath it all there were clearly some troubling issues. Her pursuit for the perfect 'glamourzonian' figure, a life of wealth at the expense of her own morals had corrupted her to the core. There is no amount of plastic surgery, other people's money, or validity from strangers than can bring you out of the dark unhappiness that was clearly being held within.

But she isn't showing you that, is she? She painted her 100,000 followers a life that she knew they would aspire to, knowing full well that the reality is unattainable for the majority, especially herself. We are all constantly being fed lies from within the health and fitness market with people like Perky who are given a dangerous platform to sell their image. And yet the powers that be allow it. But I will reiterate something I said earlier on in this chapter. Pinky's/Perky's story is not unique. She is not the first person to do this. And she will not be the last.

It's interesting to me that so many people complain about magazines using airbrushing on their models and yet it's now perfectly acceptable for anyone to add filters to their pictures and no one really questions it. It is no surprise to me that so many young males and females are turning to drugs to get the physiques they see on shows like *Love Island*. A year of solid work in the gym doesn't yield the results they are so fictitiously being fed by 'influencers' and the media.

Who's to blame? How can we scoff at this new generation of people who are literally making millions of pounds selling their naked bodies on OnlyFans, or making their first seven figure wage off one video on YouTube? Even as I write this some fuckwit has made a million quid selling the idea that you could lose seven pounds in seven minutes using her whack-attack abs routine.

Supermodel diets don't make you a supermodel.

Rachel's haircut from *Friends* doesn't make you Jennifer Aniston.

Getting a six-pack does not make you a personal trainer.

Brushing your teeth everyday does not make you a dentist.

Following idiots on Instagram who take selfies every five minutes will not help you get in shape.

See through the bullshit.

Ask more questions.

Look behind the scenes at who's selling you the shit you're buying and consuming.

Ultimately, look out for the Perkys of this world, because much like her own experience, when Instagram did change their algorithm, her fantasy land of instant gratification, insincere accolades and ephemeral likes started to wane. It wasn't long before the makeup started to fade and she eventually left the fitness business altogether and married one of her 'clients'. So, the moral of this story is …

Be less Perky. And be more Pinky.

EVERYBODY NEEDS GOOD NEIGHBOURS

In 2017, I occasionally found myself working a Saturday on a road in North London known as Billionaires' Row. The likes of the Sultan of Brunei, Lakshmi Mittal and the Zabludowiczs all owned houses here (though presumably didn't live there all-year round). It was a pretty big deal if you could get a client around these parts and at one point, I was working with many of the residents on the road.

However, one house in particular, or should I say one family in particular, stood out from the crowd as my source of entertainment for the week. I genuinely looked forward to getting my ass out of bed on a Saturday just so I could go and see what this household had in store for me that day.

The family I was visiting were from somewhere in eastern Europe. I could never quite tell and you never wanted to ask because these sorts of people, with this type of money, want everything to be low key …

Apart from their houses, of course. And their cars. And their yachts and expensive jewellery. You get the drift.

However, what was special about this family in particular,

wasn't the fact that they had staff for everything; it was their little bouncing seven-year-old cherub – Diego.

Diego was below average height for his age. He wasn't what I'd call a chubby kid, but he definitely didn't skip a meal. Cherubic, you might say.

He had two black slugs for eyebrows and a smile so wide that if he were to ever go into a church, all the crosses would immediately do a one eighty and tip over. He always had a devilish look in his eye as if he was going to slash your tyres or flood your basement. I never got to know what his second name was, but I'm sure it was something along the lines of Damian, Lucifer or Beelzebub. And what made it worse was that his parents (my clients) would always dress him up like Toad of Toad Hall. He'd be regularly seen in small jodhpur style trousers with a white shirt and herringbone jacket, just like little Lord Fauntleroy. The kid was a walking, talking comedy show.

I found out that Diego had been expelled from his first school at five years old. He was diagnosed with ADHD and his not-so-present mother had kept him home-schooled ever since. However, after getting to know him, I realised he was just bullshitting so he didn't have to go to school with all the normal children.

I liked this kid.

So, I did what any normal person would do. I made sure he thought I was his best friend.

The thing about kids is that if you swear in front of them or swear at them, they immediately think you're cooler than their parents. And given that everyone in the house would bow down to this hybrid monkey, I'd immediately found my comedy partner.

This little shit was as bright as a button. He'd happily spend his days giving the run around to all the staff including the head Filipina nanny who he clearly had an evil disdain for, just so he could make me laugh.

For example – one time I was standing outside in the driveway waiting for the lady of the house to finish whatever it was she was doing when Diego sneaked around the side of my car, one hand behind his back, the other holding a tennis ball aloft like he was showing me a crystal ball.

'I bet you can't throw this over my house,' he said with a smirk on his face.

'Bet I can,' I replied.

'Alright, prove it,' he said, knowing I was like Marty McFly being called 'chicken'.

Admittingly, his house was colossal. I mean it was big, big. But I'd been training power for the past year. I can throw. But even this house was too massive for me

Bugger that though, I wasn't going to let this little leprechaun beat me.

'Diego, mate, I could probably throw you over that house let alone this measly tennis ball.'

'Go on then,' he replied, knowing full well I wouldn't and couldn't. He kept smiling and goading me on.

'If you throw that ball over my house then I'll get my mum to pay you double,' he said.

Reminder, this kid was seven years old!

'OK, fine,' I replied, wondering whether his powers of persuasion could in fact get me paid double bubble.

Game on.

I took a step back, leant onto my back foot and launched the ball as hard as I could, giving myself tennis elbow at the same time.

The ball travelled nicely, soaring high. The pitch was pretty good. It veered to the left, and then I heard the dull thud of the ball hit the back of one of the east quarter towers, before bouncing off into the vast garden behind the house. Damn, the kid was right.

'See I told you, you couldn't.'

'Alright, smartarse, you do it.'

Diego smirked and then took the other hand from behind his back to reveal a shiny red cricket ball.

'You can't throw that you...'

!!!!!SMASH!!!!!

The little piece of Satan's asshole didn't wait for me to even finish my sentence, he just went straight ahead and threw the cricket ball as hard as he could at one of the large windows. He wasn't even looking to get it over the house. He was just looking for an excuse to break stuff.

Chaos quickly ensued.

Enter head nanny, the Filipina warrior with a face like she was sucking on a bitter lemon. 'MASTA DIEGO, wa tha HELL you doin, you naughty bwoy, you muvva will not like you for dis. Go say yourself sowwy,' she said (I think).

Diego was looking directly at me, grinning like the Grinch. By now more staff had entered the fray. Lots of gasps and exacerbated 'Oohs' filled the air. I got the idea this wasn't the first-time little Diego had punished the house.

'You go say yourself sowwy, you go now Masta Diego,' she said (I think), as she grabbed him by the arms and dragged him to the front door.

The following session after this debacle was a toughie. It was like being in school when you couldn't laugh in a lesson, so you just held it in and let out little yelps here and there. It also didn't help that the home gym looked out onto the garden where my tennis ball had landed. Not only had it bounced off the roof, but it had also taken out one of their birdbaths. I denied all knowledge, and if there were a dog around, I'd have blamed it on him. However, although there wasn't, there was always Diego.

This little sod's antics could easily make up a book of his own. There are so many weirdly subtle things he did and some not so subtle. Such as the time he purposefully urinated on the new kitchen his mum had spent one million quid on.

Yes, it's true.

About six months into training the family, I arrived at the house at my usual time to find the whole driveway stacked full of slick looking commercial black vehicles. After I'd squeezed in the space, I made my way through the house, hurdling over workmen who were bringing out basins and taps from the kitchen.

I only ever saw this client once a week, so since our last session she had completely demolished her kitchen and was starting afresh. Nothing more than a full house renovation, I thought. Nothing uncommon around these parts. That being said, within the session she had told me that this wasn't just some ordinary kitchen she was installing. Oh no, this was the crème de la crème of kitchens, a one-off, a gold plated, bedazzled behemoth of a kitchen that no one in the world would have apart from her. Nothing too expensive, just a cool one million pounds.

Say what now?

It had taken months for lights to be manufactured from some of the finest crystal in the world (so I was told), the taps were made of gold; the barstools were made with Venetian ink. I was scared to sit down. I mean this client was waxing lyrical about the worktop that would cost more than I could earn in five years. It was going to be the unique selling point of the house. However, what was important to her most of all was that …

No one else would have it.

And, here it is, folks. Peer pressure doesn't just happen on social media, oh no, Hampstead Garden Suburb is rife with it.

About two months later, the kitchen had been installed. I was invited to the Grand Opening. Yes, they really did have a grand opening, and to be fair it did look quite grand. Residents from the entire road swanned over. Champagne poured freely, people spoke about who and what to invest in, which politician was doing this, what grades their precious little Timmy got. And, then I noticed, in the corner of my eye, little Diego fighting the Filipina warrior by the main stairs, just slightly out of view of the guests. He was viciously fighting her off with one hand and stuffing his face with the hors d'oeuvres in the other. It was well past his bedtime, but the sneaky little shit obviously wanted to get in on the action. Everyone knew you couldn't feed Diego past midnight and you definitely shouldn't get water anywhere near him otherwise he'd multiply… and we didn't want that, did we?

The following week, I arrived on time. I was told to wait for her royal highness once again, so I took a pew in the kitchen with some of the other staff and Diego.

The same day they were having some outdoor event, so a lot of attention was directed away from the kitchen and on to the garden. People were running in and out of the house not really paying attention to what the angry Smurf was up to, or that I was clock watching. It soon became a kitchen for two and I was sat on the island opposite little Diego.

And there he was grinning again.

'Watched *Home Alone* last night,' he claimed.

'Oh, that's awesome, that's one of my favourite films. But that was made way before you were even manufactured at the *Childs' Play* factory,' I joked.

He grinned some more. I got the sneaking suspicion he was up to something. The cogs in his Stewie Griffin brain were almost certainly thinking up another cunning plan to set the home workers' heart rates into the heart attack zone.

'Whaaaat are you doing, Diego?' I asked suspiciously, as he rose from his bar stool and promptly stood on the £300,000 grand worktop. 'Get the fuck off there you little shit, you're going to get in trouble,' I said, knowing full well that if her royal highness or the Filipina warrior were to walk in, I'd get the blame or Diego would get an ass whooping.

And then what the boy wonder did next will never leave my memory.

He unzipped his corduroys, pulled out his pecker, looked at the kitchen door, looked at me and then suddenly, in the deepest voice he could muster said, 'I'm gonna give you to the count of 10, to get your ugly, yella,'no-good keister offa ma property, before I pump your guts full of lead!'

He looked again at the kitchen door, clearly waiting on an audience.

I heard footsteps…

'One … two … ten.' At this point he then proceeded to urinate all over the gold-plated kitchen sink while imitating the sound of a machine gun.

Then it happened. By the kitchen door I saw the Filipina Warrior with her mouth open and eyes alight with shock. She stood there stock still for a full thirty seconds, just watching the madness.

Instead of all hell breaking loose, which Diego would have thrived on seeing as he was born from the depths of hell itself, she put her head in her hands and walked off whimpering. 'Master

Diego, he kiwwin me. All day, all night, kiwwin me somefing tewwible. I take no more of this. I done,' she said (I think).

I'm in shock.

Alas, Diego is not in shock. He finds it hilarious.

'Keep the change, you filthy animal,' he looks at me completely deadpan.

I died.

This whole scene is cutting into my allotted PT time with his mother. It was now already fifteen minutes into the session, and I quickly made my excuses and got out of dodge before this clusterfuck was blamed on me. A gremlin pissing in a gold sink, an emotional wreck of a Filipina, her seven staff and a mother who will probably sue me for seeing her son's boyhood.

No thank you, no thank you sir. I'm out.

I left it a week before contacting the client again, just so things would hopefully blow over. However, to my surprise she booked me again without mentioning a word about the previous week; it was like nothing had ever happened. So, when the following Saturday came around, I packed my things and off I toddled wondering what hilarity was going to happen that day.

Quite the contrary, however. I arrived to find that Diego had been shipped off to his grandparents overseas for an 'extended' stay.

Bummer, it was going to be a normal session then.

I was ushered into the house the usual way but instead of being taken into the luxury kitchen for, what now seemed the normal 'wait for her royal highness to decide when she's ready', I was guided through to a sitting room I didn't even know existed. What I did notice, however, was that the luxury kitchen was now not so luxury.

No, it had nothing to do with Diego staining the gold basin. Oh, no. What I later discovered was that whoever had sold her royal highness the kitchen had duped her into thinking it was a one-off. When actually he'd gone and sold the exact same kitchen to one of her neighbours on the same road!

She wasn't having that. She wasn't having that at all. Up came the floors, the crystal, and the sink, the beautiful Venetian inked bar stools. One million pounds worth of kitchen thrown to the dogs. (I very much doubt it was even recycled.)

And so there you have it. How social psychosis can change the way we act as humans. How it can warp our sense of reality even in the richest circles. It stems far deeper than social media and photo filters. We are born with this innate sense of competition (or adherence depending on how you look at it) with our peers.

I trained the family for a few months after Pissgate but only saw Diego on a few occasions. Instead of spending time out on the naughty step he was shipped off to a naughty step overseas. The life of billionaires, eh? There is no question in my mind that Diego will go on to be a world leader or a criminal mastermind. The latter being more probable.

Given that this family's bank account had ten digits in it, the irony here was that the family had actually haggled down my prices to get a better deal (something you should never do to a professional). The final nail in the coffin though wasn't the fact I had to constantly wait for the client, or the fact they underpaid me. It was that when I was actually paid, it was in cash. In Euros.

In fucking Euros. I couldn't believe it. Not only had they got their sessions at three quarters of the going rate, they had the audacity to pay me in Euros, which I had to go and convert into pound sterling, which would also cost me money.

Needless to say, I sacked them off as clients. They didn't care, I was just another disposable worker, and so it was on to the next one for me. But they wouldn't have the last laugh. No way.

I picked up the phone and contacted the neighbour over the road who had duplicated their kitchen and offered my services.

I spent the next year training them. It was a whisk I was willing to take.

PART EIGHT
VALUED AND DEVALUED

LESSON EIGHT:

Starting your days at 4.30am has some positives. You'll miss the traffic, you'll know what it feels like to be a bat, you'll get to see the result of what alcohol and ketamine can do the morning after. And, if you work in Hampstead, you'll probably get to see more doggers in one morning than most people will see in a lifetime. If you are offered to trade all that in for working on a yacht in the middle of the Caribbean, it's better to stay humble.

Throughout my life so far, I have never been much good at anything unless it was to do with being creative or sporty. It was safe to say that I'd never become a dentist, doctor, lawyer or an accountant.

Being the best at art, design, drama and PE when you're at one of the top UK schools, doesn't lend much to the out-of-date exam-based curriculum, which gets rammed down our throats from early childhood. Being surrounded by cerebral academics whose sole purpose at school was to get as many A*s as they possibly could was no easy feat when all you wanted to do was paint pictures, write words or score a goal. It's no wonder that after leaving school, spending a year of looking at pretentious paintings of awkward nudes at art school, and three years studying Industrial Design at university, that I'd end up in a low-paid, undervalued industry such as design. However, it prepared me well for the years ahead of becoming a personal trainer.

See, the life of a PT seems like a pretty good deal, right? A sense of freedom without too many constraints. A life where you get to train all day, live well, get paid loads, and ultimately be your own boss. We don't have to wear suits or put up with pencil necks delegating their rubbish menial tasks day in day out.

The idea is nice. But the reality is so far from the truth you wouldn't believe it.

According to the latest Statista report, there are over 22,000 registered personal trainers in the UK, with the majority of these working in insecure jobs on a freelance basis. Eighty per cent of those lack the professional training and 90 per cent of them quit within the first year.

The allure doesn't match the reality. But why?

Well, most personal trainers start because they love training themselves in the gym. They make their hobby their profession. Mistake number one. They soon realise that clients don't appear out of thin air and so they end up applying for jobs in main chain gyms where there's an abundance of clients to be tapped up. These main chain gyms have managers who only care about performance and number quotas. When you don't meet those quotas you, as the PT, end up losing out. You're now working for the man again, the pencil-necks that are taking more than 50 per cent off what you earn per client, and then whack you with a huge rent to pay on top of it. Mistake number two. If that doesn't finish you off and you decide to go freelance, you now have to find the clients yourself and pay rent and pay your own taxes and National Insurance contributions. Trust me, its never-ending.

It's a long road and very few do well out of it.

Being valued is an important part of anyone's mental health. Validation is a key part of that (which maybe is why social media has seen its success), and personal trainers more than most come into, or face, situations on a daily basis where they are valued and devalued. You might think that anyone who works in any industry that is client-facing gets a good feel as to whether they are valued or not, but personal trainers are exactly that – personal. We don't just train, we listen, we care, we are the unofficial psychologists of most clients. And in my case, a urogenital consultant – thanks L.

Personal trainers build a relationship with clients over time which many industries never get. Training is not like going to the doctors or liaising with your lawyer. We see people day in, day out, on a regular basis in an intimate environment. I've seen more tits and asses and genitalia than a pornstar's fluffer. I've seen more shit, puke and sweat than most adults have had hot dinners. I get to know my clients better than most people know their closest, oldest friends. And that is why we cannot help but take things personally when we feel devalued, and I can assure you I have had a multitude of shit clients over the years devalue my service, devalue my business and devalue me as a person. I have put up with countless clients answering their phones in sessions, those that persist in driving down your prices to get better deals, those that chop and change their sessions and argue about paying cancellation fees. There are those who sometimes shit on you (literally) and there are those who think you are an employee of theirs and so they can order you around like a recruit in a North

Korean army camp. I've even had two clients demand refunds on their blocks of sessions after I herniated my third disc because I'd become a 'defunct' trainer. To those who seek to devalue you, and what you do, you are seen as disposable.

And then there's the flip side. Being valued.

There is nothing like it. There is nothing like changing someone's life for the better and them thanking you for it. Whether it's aesthetically or mentally, someone telling you that you've done a good job is one of the reasons why I stayed a PT for almost twenty years. I have been incredibly lucky in my career, but I'd sooner choose a birthday card from a client showing genuine care, than given permission to drive their supercar. FACT.

Being devalued is something that is rife in the fitness industry and it doesn't need to be. Know your worth. Know that what you're doing should be respected. Yes, you might lose a little cash in the short term if you get rid of a client but job longevity, hell, job satisfaction, comes from respecting yourself and respecting what it is you do. In an industry where we can invoice people for wasting our time, do NOT lower your prices to people who undervalue you. Work on your schedule, NOT someone else's. And under no circumstance do you ever … ever, ever, *ever,* let anyone tell you that you need to clean up his or her faeces.

In short, be more like Milo.

MILO

It was late 2017, around 7am, when I received a phone call from a very secretive 'concierge' company who were calling from the Middle East. I remember it well because the only time I ever receive phone calls that early in the morning is from clients who are about to cancel.

It was an unusual time, and an unusual phone call.

'Hi there, am I speaking to Matt Hodges?'

I replied yes, realising this wasn't a client.

'Hi Matt, great to talk to you. My name is Bob. I've been given your details through a contact on LinkedIn with regards to an exclusive client of mine who is looking to offer a very unique personal training opportunity.'

If you're a user of LinkedIn I'm sure you all probably know that we get a lot of this type of thing. If it's not someone asking me to try their new fitness equipment apparatus or some douche trying to get me to buy into a multi-level marketing nutrition scam, it'll be a Prince Babatunde telling me that he has 30million US dollars in a Western Union account for me. All I need to do is give him my bank details so he can render me homeless.

However, in true personal trainer eager-beaver style, my ears prick up at the words 'exclusive opportunity'.

I'm all ears.

The call was from a legitimate concierge company who had an incredibly wealthy client looking for a *female* personal trainer to be an on-board crewmember on his private yacht for the coming summer (UK winter).

Well, as you can hopefully guess by now, I'm not female, so why were they calling me you might wonder?

At the time I had a number of trainers working for me, two of whom were female.

After the call, I'd learnt that the client's PA would be in London in the next two weeks conducting interviews on behalf of her employer. It was arranged that I would go to the interview first to sell our wares, and to see if any of my female trainers would be suitable for the job.

That same week, I prepared my pitch and went to the famous Savoy hotel where the PA greeted me. The magnitude of the job became very apparent very quickly.

I was greeted at the front desk by one of the representatives from the concierge company, and two men dressed in all white thawbs and dark sunglasses. After the usual meet and greet, I was escorted upstairs to one of the presidential suites.

After passing two more burly Arab men, I entered through the door to a hallway that stretched out longer than my entire house, which gave way to an expanse of glass overlooking the Strand and Victoria Embankment Gardens. The immaculately decorated room flowed from the living quarters through to the dining area, passing a small mahogany bar that had been built into the walls. Antique black wooden furniture adorned with gold leaf was littered around the room, standing side by side with modern sculptures giving the suite a regal, yet contemporary feel. I was used to luxurious places like this with my existing clientele, so I didn't give off the usual wonderment that they had been accustomed to from some of the personal trainers who had arrived before me.

'Are you not impressed?' a small female voice called out from the living room area.

Sitting there perched on the edge of an orange suede sofa

was a small middle eastern lady, immaculately dressed with fine jewels and Versace head scarf.

'You must be Matt,' she said, as she took my hand. The smell of her Oud was somewhat overpowering, so I took a polite step back to where I was being directed to sit.

'Thank you for coming, would you like a drink?' she asked.

Before I could answer, a young, good-looking Persian male waiter was already hovering at my shoulder offering me a tall crystal tumbler filled with spring water and cucumber.

It would have been impolite to say no. This was either a rea-life scene from a James Bond movie and I was about to get poisoned or they realised that the overbearing bodyguards were putting the guests off.

After what I can only describe as the second most surreal meeting I have ever had, it became clear what the job entailed.

The incredibly wealthy Arab businessman had just built a high-end gym on his yacht, and now wanted an on-board personal trainer whilst he sailed the Caribbean over the summer months. He already had a strong crew, but this was the final position he wanted to fill. The job paid £70k tax free, with board and food included. The job role required two PT sessions a day, nutrition needed to be overseen with the head chef, and all guests on board would be allocated a private training session. The only stipulation was that the trainer had to be female.

Alarm bells.

Well, even if you can't hear them, I did.

Not comfortable feeling like a pimp, I thought it only fair to bring the female PTs I knew directly into the second round of interviews. However, the two trainers that I had working for me were incredibly busy and I was reluctant to take them off their current jobs for something that seemed fishy. I had to think of possible alternatives.

At the time, there were only a handful of women working at the central London gym. None of them really needed my business and I knew none of them would take on a full-time job. Out of the potential three I could use, there was only Pinky who was a complete no for reasons you've already read. She'd either end up taking selfies on the yacht all day or shagging the client and then charging him for it. Which, to be fair, he probably wouldn't have minded.

The other female trainer I knew was a real-life ex porn star, so she too was out. I needed someone who wasn't going to end up taking advantage or being taken advantage of. I needed a person who could hold her own. Someone who wasn't garish, someone who went under the radar, someone who could get the job done and keep a smile on her face but took no shit, no matter what.

That, of course, was Milo. The girl who would sooner give you the shirt off her back than let you go without. A girl who cared for every single person she ever met, a girl who when her chips were down would always pick them back up again. A girl who in previous weeks had already expressed her desire to find a way out of the fitness industry. It was a perfect fit. If you had a glass that was half empty, Milo would be there to fill it up for you. I would literally walk barefoot across a desert of Lego for this girl for the number of times she helped me out.

More than just the body of *Baywatch*, and the face of *Crimewatch* (our inside joke), she was the perfect candidate. She was a great PT, and readily accepted the invitation for her own interview, which, by all accounts, went swimmingly.

Two weeks passed and we were both waiting in 'textpectation' on our phones to be told whether we had the contract or not. Milo was going to make a swift £65,000 for this job, and I would take my cut of £5,000 for the referral. Lo and behold, Milo got the job, and was to depart in a week's time.

In the days that followed Milo's departure, people felt the hollow void at the studio. The smiling, bubbly, glass-half-full character had left for pastures new and was getting paid handsomely for it. I received regular updates from the concierge company as to how she was doing, while simultaneously FaceTiming Milo, so everyone was kept in the loop as to her whereabouts.

After about two weeks, when Milo had reached Antigua with the rest of the crew, the contact started to fall by the wayside. This was to be expected. Milo wasn't beholden to me, and she was obviously getting on with the job and living her best life.

That was until about four weeks into her trip when she FaceTimed me late at night.

'Matt, I'm not sure how long I can do this for,' she said with a solemn look on her face.

'What's wrong? Tell me he hasn't done anything to you has he? Is everything OK?' I asked, genuinely worried for her welfare.

'Yeah, of course, everything's fine, it's just well ...' Milo stumbled to find the precise words. 'He's just a bit of a fuck, really. Just a fuck on a yacht,' she said, matter of fact.

'What ... does ... that ... mean?' I asked.

'Nothing, in particular. He's just a self-serving, overweight goon who treats people badly. Oh, yeah, and he's got more hair than a Dulux dog. The stuff is everywhere,' she carried on. 'I found a tonne of what I think are his pubes in my pillow case last night. God knows how they got there but they've got the unmistakable scent of bad cologne on them, so I suspect he's been using my pillow,' she said with a nervous laugh.

'What do you mean he treats people *badly*?' I asked, hoping that I wouldn't have to involve the concierge.

'Well, let me tell you,' she began. 'On the first night, he sacked one of the stewardesses for not ordering enough of the specialist tequila he liked. Two days later, he berated one of the female staff members for lining up his prayer mat the wrong way. A week later, he ordered everyone off the boat and left us on one of the islands for five hours whilst he binge watched his favourite series. The next week he sacked a deckhand because he took his top off on deck. The week after, he clogged up the shower with his back hair and made two of the girls clean it out with their bare hands. I mean, the list goes on and on ...'

'Has he personally treated you badly, Milo?' I asked, knowing that I may have to go into the gun safe and get my Purdeys.

'Well, nothing other than shouting "Oi, girl!" at me all the time. Slightly irritating. He's also always asking me why I'm not married, asking me why I don't wear much makeup, that sort of thing,' she replied, playing down her disappointment. After an hour-long conversation I had calmed her down and put the shotguns back in the safe. She was going to ride it out and see where it went.

To my amazement, two weeks later, who do you think rolled back into the gym?

Milo of course. A super-tanned version of Milo.

After a solid hour of everyone trying to chew her ear off as to why she was back, I eventually got her on her own and took her for coffee. I hadn't heard anything from the concierge company, so I was perplexed as to why she was standing in front of me when she was meant to be sailing the seven seas. It had turned out that she, along with some of the other crew, had packed her bags and made her own way back to the UK.

'Matt, you're not going to believe what happened. His demands started to get out of control. Telling the deckhands to wash his underwear by hand, that sort of thing. The captain of the boat didn't stick up for the crew, so some of them packed their bags and left. It meant that I had to start filling in on some of the jobs. I didn't really care too much, I mean, I'm on a lovely yacht in the Caribbean – I'll make the most out of it, I thought.'

I was wondering where this was going. I could never imagine Milo getting sacked, she was just too nice, and good, for that. Something truly hideous must have happened for her to up and leave.

'So, knowing that he had pissed a lot of the crew off and half of them had left, the hairy owner just started taking advantage of the people left on the boat. He knew that we either needed the money or were too scared to leave,' she said.

I was worried about where this was going. I've met my fair share of nasty people who take advantage of situations where they think they are in control. I will always even out the odds. As you already know, I'm not afraid to give a small, polite and calm word in their ear, to tell them that no matter how rich and wealthy they are, when they are out on the street, they are equal. It's a nice little leveller.

Yes, I felt overly protective.

'Tell me he didn't touch you, did he, Milo?' I asked, ready

to wage war.

'Hell no, no, of course not. No. That's not what happened at all. No, well, what really happened, well, was, well, kind of embarrassing, really,' she said timidly. 'Well, he took a dump – a proper shit – on the floor of his bedroom and wanted me to clean it up for him.'

I looked at Milo dumbfounded. 'I'm sorry… what now?' I replied flabbergasted.

'Yeah exactly, he took a poo right in the middle of his *own* bedroom. On the floor. A steaming wet pile of shit. Then, he had the cheek to ask me to clean it up.'

I was completely baffled. It was like one of tsohe tmies wehn you wree cnofnused as fcuk but you unedrsotod eyrveinhtg giong on aournd you.

What was it with all these clients shitting and pissing themselves? I thought.

'Yes babe, the hairy bastard took a shit on his floor. I'm not kidding. Dirty sod, he was. And, judging by his shit, he needs a lot more fibre.' Milo took a large gulp of her coffee. 'That was the end for me, obviously. I'm not being undervalued like that. No matter how much he pays me, I draw a line at that, so I left.'

'Oh, mate, you've had an absolute Weston Super. What did he do when you said no? Why would he shit on his own bedroom floor on his own a multi-million-pound yacht? It makes … no … sense.'

'Absolutely shocking, isn't it? When mum found out she rang the concierge company and complained. They sent me some remuneration hush money, so all is not lost, I guess, but I won't be going on any private yachts any time soon. It was a great experience, and I learnt a lot from it, so thank you for the opportunity,' Milo said, spoken in true Milo 'glass half full' style.

'How can I make it up to you, mate?' I asked. I felt bad, even though I could never have predicted this. 'Do you want me to call the concierge company and complain about the hairy monstrosity as well?' I felt like I owed Milo more. I'd put her in the job, and I wanted to take responsibility for her being in that horrible situation.

'No, no, no, don't worry about it, Matt, really. It's all good. I still got paid, a lot, it was a good experience. It was good for my confidence and, you know, there's always a light at the end of the tunnel. All is not lost.'

'What do you mean?' I asked, intrigued as to what she was thinking.

'I now know for sure that I won't take crap from anyone. I know my worth. And without this experience, I would never have learnt that – so thanks.'

I could see something had changed in Milo – she had come to understand her own value. And there's a lesson there for all of us – if you don't know your own value, your own worth, you'll be treated like shit.

'And anyway at least we can say that we now know Sasquatch has finally been found.'

MADE IN CHELSEA

I truly believe that you meet people for a reason. If you enter my life, and vice versa, chances are it was meant to happen. I believe that if you work hard enough, have enough luck, or stick around long enough to gain experience, people will arrive in your life destined to change it.

In this instance, it was the end of summer 2018. The Three Amigos, plus our fourth wheel Kane, had gone out on an informal social because Irish wanted to tell us all something. It was important apparently. We were expecting him to tell us his new personal best on the bench press, or that Smirnoff had in fact given him a yearly membership gold card, but instead, to our surprise, his announcement was about to take him in a new direction.

'Fellas, oi have decided dat its time ta leave the PT game. Me brother has set up in Sydney and oi have decided that next year O"m goin' ta be joinin' him. Me mammy said dat O"m drinkin' too much and Oi have a problem. Christ on a bike, she even said dat O"m turnin' into me father, and just like him, that alcohol does not solve any of me problems.'

I suspect that the final straw was finding Meat's pulsating penis trainer, but the jury is still out on that one. Irish had spoken about leaving the industry for a while now and all it took was a new opportunity for him to bite the bullet. Much like Milo, it was time for Irish to move on. He'd fallen out of love with the fitness game and the new breed of PTs who were now flooding it. Danger and Kane knew all too well that they were nearing the end spectrum of the personal training profession too. I, on the other hand had been squirrelling away, intent on finding another studio of my own to set up. It had been a while since my last one, business was good, and it was time to make a break for it myself again. More on this later.

However, it's worth remembering here again just how the PT industry had changed beyond recognition in just a few years. Professional PTs with qualifications and experience and an understanding of the body had been replaced by amateur social media influencers who didn't care to learn about body mechanics. Being in your mid/late thirties in an industry bustling with young blood makes you look at it from a different perspective, so we were all somewhat envious of Irish's new life that awaited him down under.

'Well, there's only one way we've got to send this out, boys,' Danger said with a devilish look in his eye. 'Let's make the most of tonight, and then we'll arrange a good old send-off next year. I've got a client holding an art evening tonight in Chelsea. There will be loads of top totty there I'm sure of it. Let's bounce down to that and gate-crash it. She won't mind.'

And so, later that evening, off we went in a taxi to the art show in South West London.

Bearing in mind that we had Kane with us, we probably should have thought this through a bit more, because upon arriving at the venue it took all of about three minutes before Kane started an altercation with the door staff.

'Listen fellas, I'm not fuckin' messin' around now, you're letting me in and there's nothing you can do about it, I'm an art critic, I know about these things,' he said, widening his feet getting ready for a punch on. If ever there were a chance to bare fists, Kane would be the first in the queue. 'I've got good money, I have. Don't believe me? Watch me buy one of these arty-farty pieces, you don't know who I am, sunshine, I've got money to spend here,' he continued having an argument with himself, a point that would come back to haunt him later in the evening. I couldn't ever imagine why the door staff couldn't see that he was an art critic who used the word 'arty-farty', but anyway.

After what seemed like an eternity of to-ing and fro-ing with the door staff, Danger calmed things down and we were all allowed into the venue, where the upper echelons of the super wealthy Chelsea brigade greeted us. Albeit hesitantly.

Pearl necklaces adorned the super skinny necks of the blonde Sloany pony pack. Stiff upper-lipped gents dressed in black velvet jackets with red socks walked past, spluttering over their long glasses of Dom Perignon. Gold signet pinkie rings looked like they were the required prerequisite to obtaining an invite to this show, and to top it off there was so much air kissing it was like oxygen was having an 'airgasm'. There were many instances of 'Hello, sweety-darling,' and 'Oh, your dress is to die for'.

The riffraff had entered the building. And we stood out like four bodybuilders at a dwarf convention.

Personally, I avoid events where I know I'll be greeted by large groups of people, but I had to make the most of it. It was going to be one of those nights where you had to master the art of manners. You know, one of those times when you're smiling and nodding, but all you want to do is to slap these spiffing knobbers in the face.

No? Well, maybe that's just me.

Clearly in the wrong place, and completely out of our comfort zone, the Three Amigos plus Kane decided the congregation point was the free bar. After a few drinks, the Amigos dispersed into the crowd and we all got into our respective 'modes' to try and get through the night.

Danger began by chatting up his client and her bunch of hot and haute friends.

Irish got busy telling some guy in a kilt that his tartan wasn't legitimate and that his own Celtic colours were brighter, more handsome, and had better blood stock.

Kane, now transformed from street pugilist to art curator,

pretended to look interested in a painting on the wall that a short lady with thick-rimmed glasses was trying to sell him. Given that I had studied fine art at Chelsea Art College for a year, I'd become accustomed to pretentious bullshit, so I chimed in on the piece.

'Yes, it's a great juxtaposition of light versus dark, hero vs demon. I feel like the artist is trying to portray a disunion of feelings here. A feeling of escapism through abstractism. What do you think, Kane?' I knew full well that Kane probably hadn't got a clue what I was talking about, and his face said it all. I tried hard not to laugh, knowing that he was probably thinking of six different ways he could execute his revenge on me afterwards. To say he was unimpressed was an understatement.

'Yes, yes, I agree,' he said looking at me with burning eyes.

'Wonderful,' said the bespectacled art connoisseur. 'What is it you agree on?' she continued.

Kane put his hand to his chin, like he was actually trying to think of a sensible answer. Instead, in true Kane fashion, never one to back down from anything or to prove a point. 'You know what, I'll take it. Bag it up, write me a receipt, I'm having this one,' Kane announced to my dismay, trying to bypass his lack of art knowledge.

'Oh excellent,' the lady said, overjoyed that she'd probably made her first sale of the evening. 'I'll go and ring this up for you. What a delight. You've bought a really great piece there. Thank you. Thank you. How would you like to pay, sir?' she said trying to finalise the bill of sale.

Kane looked at me with intent. I've seen happier Jews in a pig farm, but I was finding this utterly hilarious. This little piggy had been sent straight to the comedy store abattoir. Kane was now a grand lighter that evening, and I knew I was in for it as soon as the sales clerk had rung it through. Luckily for me, however, impressed with my complete and utter bullshit description of the colourful skidmark Kane had just purchased, a highly drunk aristocratic couple approached me and engaged in small talk. It seemed I was saved from the impending doom that awaited me.

'We overhead your jolly good description of the piece of art that your gentlemen friend just purchased. Are you a dealer yourself, what, what?' (I added that last bit in there for shits and giggles. A 'what-ho' could have sufficed but it may have pushed the posh a little too far).

'No, not at all, I studied fine art at Chelsea Art College many years ago, though,' I knew this would be my 'in'.

Suddenly, I was one of 'them'. I might not be wearing a pinkie signet ring or wearing pink chinos, but I was now a token toff for the evening. I swear to you, I even think my yesses became 'ya's' and I suddenly felt compelled to tell people that 'we should do lunch sometime'. It was a chameleon-like change, not too dissimilar to when the builders come round your house and you start throwing out 'aint's' and 'geeza's'. We are the masters of adaptation, us personal trainers.

The husband, noticing Kane burning a hole in the back of my head with his demon eyes, turns to him and says, 'Young lad, you need to smile more, you've just bought a ruddy excellent piece.'

'You need to fuck off more,' Kane replied, turning away, knowing he'd now have to go and pay for the painting.

'Charming,' the wife replied, turning back to me. 'So, what is it that you do then? And your name is …?'

The next couple of hours were spent talking everything health and fitness related. Ironic, given that these two were chugging Dom Perignon faster than a toupee in a hurricane. Danger had sloped off somewhere with his client. A comatose Irish had to be escorted off the premises, thus proving his mother right. Kane was now proudly presenting his new piece of art to the door staff, and I was left talking the logistics of training the couple's high achieving children five times a week at their gated Chelsea mansion. As I mentioned at the beginning of this chapter, it always fascinates me how you pick up clients. Here I was, going from gate-crashing an art show with three degenerate friends to now signing a new client and booking in a potential two-grand a month.

The couple had high aspirations for their children and revelled in the fact that they went to one of the best schools that money could buy. They were eager to get their children into peak fitness and would pay whatever it took to get them there. After we'd agreed an initial session, I said my goodbyes to all the Arabellas, the Digbys and the Ruperts with the usual folly of 'we must do this again sometime' (aka I'm never going to see you again, let alone call you). In two weeks' time, I'd be pitching up to their gated mansion in Chelsea, giving sessions to a 7-year-old girl and a 10-year-old boy.

I'd trained children before now and they are always some of the most rewarding clients to train. If you make it fun, kids listen, but the key is to find out what makes them tick. For instance, the two children I was being employed to train were nothing short of bloody useless at anything sport related. Their whole lives had been focussed on academia, which their parents had promoted. Not to be outdone by any of their peers, the two children were subjected to a vigorous timetable. They were up at 6.30am before breakfast to play 30 minutes on their grand piano. They would then be chaperoned to school until 4pm, from where they would come home, have an early dinner and then have another hour's tuition. They would then see me for 60 minutes, which left a couple of hours before bed, which would constitute them either going over their day's work or reading to their parents in the evening. Then on weekends, they had Sunday school and another hour each of tuition. The children were brainboxes to say the least, and very far from sports orientated.

It was clear from the outset that I'd need to find a different angle for these kids. The poor little grommets were incredibly ill-coordinated, which makes life quite difficult for non-sporty folk. Traditional methods of exercise like resistance training or PE were wasted on these two as it left them frustrated, and their parents even more frustrated that they weren't excelling in something. Time after time both the kids would come to me highly stressed and often lash out at each other. They weren't enjoying the sessions, and after a hard day of head in the books they needed something fun that they could enjoy.

Something needed to change, and I had the solution.

In the basement of their beautiful Chelsea townhouse sat an

immaculate 20-metre azure pool, which was completely wasted. They told me they rarely went in it.

It was to be my way of finding their fitness mojo.

After agreeing that I would take the kids in a different direction with their fitness, I managed to get both of them in the pool and taught them how to swim. In a short period of time, I had both the kids swimming at school competition level.

They were incredible; a switch had been turned on. Both kids took to the water like ducks to a pond, or in their case, swans to their summer estate lake. There was a noticeable change in both of their moods, they weren't fighting between each other anymore and they would often want to come down to the sessions early and leave late. Swimming was something that was a release for them, and the bonus was that they were really good at it. I'd taken them under my wing and felt like they were some of my greatest transformations. I had turned their vulnerability into fortitude, and they were becoming stronger for it. However …

There was a minor detail in this little trifecta of awesomeness that would derail their training, and ultimately send me on the start of a downhill spiral.

The father.

I'd been training the kids for six months and they were nearing the end of their school year. I was now well and truly in with their Chelsea 'set' and was invited to their end of year sports day. Sometimes being valued means being included. I was seen as part of the family and was allowed to attend one of the most sensitive family events. There have been other times like this where being included meant more than any monetary reward for a job.

However, because I'd spent so much time with these kids, this was one that I thought I would relish the most. Unfortunately, it would also be my downfall.

See, the thing is, ladies and gentlemen, swimming doesn't really cross over with sprinting or long distance running, shot putting, or javelin throwing. There is no pool on the sports day athletics field. And, after two hours of watching both kids fail miserably at all the sprinting events, the look on the father's face was what I can only describe as having shit on his top lip. He was unimpressed to say the least.

I knew. I knew right there and then that this was the end for the kids … and me. There was something so deep rooted in the event that I had missed. This day wasn't about the kids participating, or even just being there and having fun with their friends. No, this was about the parents' bragging rights that their kids weren't only bookworms, but also sporting champions. It was a feather to their bow that had floated effortlessly away in the wind … alongside my employment.

'What on earth has happened?' came the father's first comment.

I knew we were about to have an awkward conversation. I knew that these two parents were going to disregard all the effort, time and patience I had invested in getting their kids to competition level swimming. And do you know what was the most annoyingly ironic thing about this? It was that they never actually ended up competing; the father was so angry that this had been their focus, he had refused to let them compete, for fear of further perceived failure. All they cared about, unbeknown to me, was the result at sports day.

'I'm really disappointed in you, Matthew,' the mother said, looking at me indignantly.

I fought my corner hard and I made it very clear what had happened from the start. I did this in earshot of everyone else around because I knew how far this would travel in these circles. Here I was at one of the most prestigious schools in the world, having a face-off with two fucked up parents, adamant that I was the reason why their kids can't run.

Well, my middle finger salutes you, I'm off.

During the following weeks there was little to no contact, other than me chasing the family for the £4,000 of unpaid personal training sessions they still owed me.

'We've decided your hourly rate is ridiculous, and we are not prepared to pay. We will give you half out of good will and that'll be the ruddy end of it,' they told me. I specifically remember this being said to me by the father over the phone.

'Er, that's not how it works. You knew my rate from the start. If I do a job in 60 minutes, it's because I've spent the last 12 years learning how to do that job in 60 minutes. You owe me for the years, not the minutes.' I already had this reply scripted, knowing full well the conversation that was to follow. I knew I should have fought my corner harder, but you cannot argue with these idiots. They will drag you down and beat you with experience, and I eventually succumbed to the 50 per cent rate drop.

But the thing is, I wasn't interested in being devalued by anyone anymore. If they saw no value in my expertise and the benefit it had on their kids, then there was no choice for me but to leave. They thought they had won by cutting me by two grand, but they'd lost the long game. It is vital to remember that at the end of the day, when the game is over, the king and the pawn go into the same box, and this was my leveller. I didn't really need any more hassle as I had my sights set on my new shiny studio which happened to be in the pipeline.

It's been a good few years since I've seen the family but I hear that the kids are excelling and the parents are still probably drunk and/or high on anti-depressants. Retrospectively I can now look at the situation from afar, and I've noticed that the upper classes aren't really that much different from the lower classes. They both walk around their estates, half pissed, mostly on drugs, hating their lives and breaking things.

TRISH

F ast forward nine months to early 2019. It was time to say
goodbye to Irish. He was off to pastures new in the land
Down Under. I cannot say that I wasn't envious. In that
period of time, I had moved to a new studio around the corner
from Danger who had remained at the Central London gym
whilst my potential new studio was being organised. Kane, well he
had gone missing … literally. To this day, no one has heard from
him or knows of his whereabouts. He vanished into thin air. I like
to think he's been recruited into the art world, or he's counselling
young Tourette's sufferers, or maybe even taken a vocation as a
Buddhist monk, but it is more than likely he's moved into a job
where hate is the required qualification. Nightclub bouncer, Debt
Collector, or Gulag officer maybe?

Either way, it felt like the end of an era, as we were also
about to give Irish his send off. Much like Milo's faux leaving do,
the beer and the vodka flowed down the chins of depraved PTs
like Rapunzel's golden hair; it wouldn't have been right to send
him off any other way.

However, things were not so bright on my side of life. There
had been hard times before in my career; I'd opened and closed a
studio; I had struggled financially; I had parted ways with more

people than a prison front gate. But for some reason, the older I got and the wiser I became about the industry my mental health declined. In the previous nine months my back injury had begun to haunt me in a very serious way. As anyone with any knowledge of serious lower back pain will attest, you think about it 24/7. It's all you think about. And when the only thing you can think about is the pain you are in, it changes you in a very negative way. My temper became short, I was withdrawing from social events and I couldn't even drive for longer than twenty minutes for fear of not being able to stand up properly when exiting the car. The pain became a nightmare. It got so bad I couldn't wear a light rucksack – the fear of pain was too much to bear, let alone shifting weights for clients. I was worried that my body had given up, and I was slowly starting to lose the physique I boasted in my twenties. I was eating too much comfort food, eating away my feelings, and doing less and less exercise because I couldn't walk properly, let alone run. This is incredibly demoralising when you are working in health, fitness, and let's be honest, the beauty industry.

On top of that, my good friend Milo had all but gone, and Irish had sought out a new adventure. My support network, the guys I had grown up with in the industry, were moving on because they knew the fitness industry could not serve them like it used to. I was being left behind. I also couldn't help but feel let down by the growing number of clients who felt they could devalue my services, my worth. In the last few years, there had definitely been a shift in the behaviour of my clients – they felt they deserved more for less, and that they owned me. I put it down to these changes happening to everybody in society – everyone has become more entitled, everyone takes more, gives less. I was certain I was coming to the end of my time as a personal trainer.

The following day, amid a hangover from hell, and high on Diazepam and Codeine for the pain, little did I know that I was about to meet a new client who would change the way I thought about things … forever.

Again.

Say hello to … Trish.

Trish was a short Scottish woman in her late fifties. Born in Aberdeen and raised from working class stock, she'd made it big in the world of law. Visually she was a trendy media sort, a stereotype of all of the things you'd associate with a gig going, Glastonbury-attending, *NME* reading music mogul. Dressed in leopard print and Dr Martens, she didn't fit the typical lawyer stereotype, that's for sure. However, what was more noticeable was that she used to sport a small pink bob wig and tattooed eyebrows. When she told me she had survived breast cancer, a lot of things clicked.

Whilst I was feeling down in the dumps about my own situation and wavering mental and physical health, I couldn't help but feel humbled. Trish had brought me back down to earth; facing a cancer survivor gave me a much-needed reality check. Not only did she look and feel great after suffering an arduous time with breast cancer, but also her attitude to life was intoxicating. With a humour that filled every dark chasm of my own degradation, we got on like a house on fire from the moment she entered my studio.

After the rigmarole of going through all the doctor's notes, it was time for Trish's body composition to be taken. Standing on the scales waiting to be measured, Trish looked at herself in the mirror, pondering her own physique while I worked around her.

'Clearly your mirror is telling me I'm pregnant,' she said jokingly, forcibly distending her own stomach.

'You're in great shape, Trish,' I said, trying to reassure her that she really was in great shape.

'Well, what are the scales saying? I'm not looking down for fear of rejection. If it doesn't tell me what I want to hear, you're to put that little prick in the corner and I'll wait for it to apologise.'

The thing was, Trish really was in good shape; she wasn't carrying an ounce of fat on her.

'You've got really low body fat for your age, Trish, you should be pleased.'

'Well, what does that mean? That I can have pizza tonight?'

'I really wouldn't advise eating something like that late at night, to be honest. Not only will you get bloated, but it'll give you the shits too.'

'If you're not meant to eat late at night, then what the hell has a fridge got a light in it for?' she asked, genuinely wondering about the answer.

'Fair point,' I said, moving on to the actual training part.

Given that she had really low body fat and was in good condition, you'd generally expect there to be some level of high-performance exercise. Wrong. When it came to training, Trish would try every excuse to do as little as possible. She knew that she wasn't going to be the next superwoman. She knew that she was, in her own words 'Not lazy, just highly motivated to do nothing.' Her illness had given her a total realisation of her abilities, where and what she wanted in life, and why she did the things she did. And she made no excuses for it. It was a breath of fresh air knowing that I wouldn't be getting the sack after ten weeks of training because she hadn't met some highly unrealistic goals she'd set herself.

So, why did she want a PT?

Trish recognised that personal trainers (good personal trainers) were more than just there to dish out sets, reps and tempos. She needed a companion who she could trust her health with who wasn't a doctor, a nurse, or a clinician reminding her of her own mortality. I was someone who she could enjoy exercising with and someone she could throw banter at who wasn't going to remind her of the dark side her recovery. I was her guided, controlled release in a world that probably felt incredibly frightening. But you would never know with Trish. You would never know if she was suffering or if she was feeling the strain of the illness that she had nearly recovered from. She always put on a brave face. She was always smiling, always laughing, and always willing to rip me a new one about the way I looked, or the failing relationship I was in.

'Most people your age are on baby number two, and yet you're still on Mambo number five, now, why is that?'

'Not for me, I'm afraid. I mean, kids are cool and all, but other people's kids are better, you can give them back and not have to worry about them sneezing in your face or asking for a lift somewhere.'

'I like your style,' she said.

We were on the same wavelength.

Over the course of a few months, we were training together twice a week. I looked forward to our sessions. Her physical results were by the by. We had a mutual understanding of what these sessions meant for her, but I still always pushed it to the point where she felt like she had actually done something to help her bone structure during her recovery.

While things were looking brighter for Trish, my world was growing darker.

Irish had set up home in Sydney, and by all accounts he loved his new life. I rarely heard from Danger, and the new studio I was at only had a handful of young trainers. I didn't mix much with them because, quite frankly, I'd become an old bore who was permanently injured and they didn't understand what living in permanent pain felt like. It was all 'go hard or go home' and if you didn't go hard in the weights room then you were a 'fake trainer'. These were the type of annoying douchebags who lived by the motto 'Eat, sleep, train, repeat'. To top it off, I was also going through the motions of the big split with my girlfriend of several years, The Great Dane. I haven't mentioned her much because it's not that story, but our demise dragged me closer to the cliff's edge.

I suddenly felt drastically alone and I couldn't really turn to anyone.

Except Trish.

Over the course of the following few weeks, I came clean to her about the way I was feeling. Within myself, the split, and how my life was panning out. This was unlike me. I would very rarely cross the boundaries of putting my personal shit onto my clients, but Trish, to her credit, always encouraged it. She asked questions about me and listened to the answers. Maybe it was a way of her forgetting about her own stuff, a way that she could feel normal with someone as fucked up as me being around her. I don't know, but whatever it was she was always there for me.

'You know what you need, don't you?' she said after

listening to me moan for several minutes.

'What's that?'

'You need a three way.'

If I had had any water in my mouth, I would have done a spit-take.

'A three-way … you know a threesome … with Ben & Jerry's. It always helps when you're depressed, believe me. Two scoops, if not the whole tub,' she winked.

And this was Trish all over. Always there to shed some light onto the darkness. I'm not sure if the boundaries of our professional relationship had been crossed, but I classed her as more of a friend.

That was until a few weeks later, when things started to change.

After an arduous session, I couldn't help but feel that she was in a bad mood. She hadn't entered the session on the best energy, and the strength work we'd completed had clearly worked her hard, if not too hard.

'Farewell shitty session, don't forget to fuck thyself on the way out,' she said clearing up her things.

'Are you OK, T? You did really well today,' I said, trying to boost her morale.

At that moment she looked at me in the eye and said nothing. It was a brief second too long and then she left without saying much. I couldn't help but feel like I'd done something to upset her. If I was one of her Scottish brethren, I felt like I would be wearing a guilt kilt, because I couldn't help but feel like I had pushed her too far. Had I? Hadn't I? Could I have done that exercise better? Could we have had another ten seconds rest? If over-thinking built muscle, then I'd be Mr Fucking Universe.

Here was a female client who I'd grown quite fond of and who seemed to be pissed off with me. All those horrible memories of clients leaving you because of some stupid little thing, started to crawl back into my psych and I couldn't handle it. Was this going to be another client who devalued me, and my style of working?

My fears were about to be realised, when, over the following two weeks, Trish failed to turn up to our sessions, and she was cancelling more and more. When she did turn up, she was slow, non-responsive and her humour had vanished. The sessions had turned from me looking forward to the hour, to dreading the awkwardness that was about to ensue. For the life of me I didn't know what had happened, but there was something clearly wrong. No matter what I said, or what I did, Trish wasn't letting me in any more, and I had no idea what was affecting her.

And then, what every PT fears the most when they value a client – she stopped coming completely.

Here I was, yet again, losing a great client because of something I thought I had done. All the raging thoughts of the 'what ifs' and the added financial pressures and the issues of being valued and devalued all flooded back.

I left it a week to let things simmer. I still hadn't heard from her, or any clarification as to why she just hadn't turned up.

I left it two weeks. Still nothing.

On the third week I reached out. I called. Nothing. I messaged. Nothing. I sent emails asking for any feedback, just so I could get an inkling as to what may have pissed her off.

Nothing.

There she was, my favourite client, just gone. How was I this disposable? How had I let myself get close to another client when I knew I could be thrown away in a heartbeat? I had spent months alone with this woman. I had seen her at her most strong, and weak. We had shared things that no one else knew about, and it was all gone in an instant. I was deflated and felt like I couldn't do it anymore.

And then the realisation hit.

It was two o'clock on a Thursday afternoon. The clouds overhead drew a glum grey over the London skyline, giving the city an air of bleakness that would make Keats proud. There was a palpable tension on the wind, and a solemn feel to the temperature that pulsated through my core. I don't know if it was a sixth sense or the nervous anxiety I had crawling through my skin, but for some reason I had already anticipated what happened next.

As I was sitting on top of Primrose Hill, looking over the

skyscrapers of Tottenham Court Road, my phone alerted me to a new WhatsApp message. It was from a name I didn't recognise, so I opened it with some trepidation.

'Hi there, I apologise if this may come as a surprise, but can I confirm that this is personal trainer Matt Hodges?'

I replied with the usual, 'Yep that's me, who is this, sorry, I don't have your number saved?' expecting it to be some spam mail of some sort.

'Hi there, my name is Paul, I am the brother of Trish; your ex-client Trish,' came the second message.

It was confirmed.

My 'ex-client'. My heart sank. There was always a glimmer of hope in me that she might come back, but no, now it was in simple black and white. I had some closure, but it still hurt. But more to the point, why was the brother of Trish contacting me? I could see he was still typing, as my heart rate started to go into spasm. Was I about to get a roasting for something I had no idea about? Was I about to be accused of something I didn't realise I did? Then this…

'I'm sorry to tell you, but Trish passed away three weeks ago. Unfortunately her treatment wasn't successful and she died suddenly. I'm sorry it has taken us so long to be in touch, but we wanted her passing to be a private affair, and so we are only now reaching out to all her business contacts to let her know.'

BAM.

I dropped the phone.

I realised that in all my time as a PT, nothing could have geared me up for this. I had never lost a client in this way. Hell, I'd never even heard of a trainer losing a client to death. This was territory I didn't understand. Immediately I felt stupid and selfish. How and why did I make it all about me? Trish was suffering in silence, and all I could think about was if I had done something wrong, if I had had to deal with yet another knock from a client, without realising that she was the one who was living in fear.

It took me a while to come to the terms with what had happened. I then remade contact with the brother. It turned out that when Trish had come to me, she had been on a drug that was being tested to see if it would work. Unfortunately, it failed, and Trish had died from the complications of later stage breast cancer.

There was no issue with me being devalued. There was no ignoring me like all the clients who had gone before. She had simply suffered in silence, affording me the time to talk about my own troubles whilst ignoring her own. And that's what kind of woman she was.

And in fitting with this narrative of coming to an end, we are gearing up for the finale of this book. I hope you have noticed that I have tried to end each chapter with a witty remark. Whilst this story is fundamentally one of sadness, I know that Trish wouldn't want to finish her story on a low point, so I'd like to share with you the slogan that she has etched into her headstone at her grave in Aberdeen, which sums up her humour perfectly:

'I was on so many pills, I hope you put a childproof lid on my coffin.'

R.I.P Trish.

THE BEGINNING OF THE END

LESSON NINE:

Don't ever give up.

The passing of Trish was the start of what turned out to be the worst year of my life. I'd learnt of her passing a month before Christmas and I was looking forward to putting the events behind me as much as my fractured mind would allow. With the turn of the New Year, I had high hopes that it was going to start better than it had ended. However, as always, the man upstairs had other plans for me. At t-minus 10 minutes after midnight, after listening to Big Ben chime, and the cacophony of thousands of people singing 'Auld Lang Syne', I rose up from my clearly too soft couch, when a surging pain struck through my tailbone and sent shockwaves down my leg. The immediate concrete-like spasm surged into my lower spine, taking my breath away – something had gone drastically wrong. As I found myself lying on the floor in agonising pain – for the fourth time – I could feel that this wasn't any ordinary back pain, this was a sign that yet another disc had blown in my back. I knew the feeling and I knew the consequences. I'd spent the last eight years nursing three disc herniations, and there I was, ten minutes into the New Year realising that yet another one had blown. How on earth could I be so unlucky? I couldn't even console myself in the knowledge that I was under the influence, or I had been doing something crazy such as fucking a porn star while dangling from a chandelier. No, I was sitting still WATCHING THE GODDAMN TV. Jools fuckin' Holland's fucking Hootenanny to be precise.

Brilliant.

A great start to the New Year, I thought. If my life could be summed up in one sentence it'd be, 'Well, that didn't go to fucking plan, did it?'

A week later, I had my diagnosis confirmed through an MRI. I had indeed herniated another disc. It was as if my spine was a line of dominoes, and some joker had tipped the end one over, watching each one fall like a never-ending pendulum of pain.

But this was just the start.

Oh boy, oh boy, was it just the start.

Because the next few months were a clusterfuck of events that ultimately nearly ended in me taking my own life. For real.

Now, I've thought long and hard about how I would write this section, and how I would tell you. And why I've waited until now, here at the end, to tell you this. The truth is, I didn't want to tell you at the beginning for fear of you thinking this would turn into some misery memoir – it isn't. That's not the book I wanted this to be, nor would you expect or want it to be. I wanted this book to be able to show the fitness industry, and my place in it. Not how fucking sad it made me, or how tragic my life would turn out. That's a lot more complicated than just blaming my life choices or blaming bad luck. As with all our lives, there are things we are accountable for, and things we're not. Me wanting to end my life was the end point of a few moments that I never could have predicted at the beginning of my career.

My warm-up to this absolute shit shower of shenanigans was admittedly self-induced, especially after all the intimate chats I'd had with Trish. These chats with Trish, a client who actually cared for me, allowed me to uncover one simple revelation …

I decided that I wasn't happy.

I was unhappy in my relationship with my girlfriend, The Great Dane.

I was unhappy with my career, my clients.

I was unhappy with my own health, my own body, my own mind.

And then Trish died, and suddenly it all came to a head.

I've never been a good one for goodbyes, which is why I always took it to heart when a client left me. However, the split with the Great Dane was so visceral, so close to home, that I couldn't help but break my own heart by breaking hers. I felt so guilty and so ashamed that I didn't have it in me to make it work that I moved out of the house I owned and let her stay there, so it didn't upend her life too much. This resulted in me sleeping on the floor of my dad's house for most of the following year. As you can appreciate, this did nothing for my declining back injury, and nothing for my current flailing emotional state.

I will explain the following events like a traditional workout, so you get an idea of the crescendo. Let's start with the warm-up, just to ease me into the impending nightmare, whereby someone had decided to crash into the back of my car whilst on their phone, writing off my car, two weeks before I was about to take it to its new owners. Luckily, no one was hurt apart from yet another jarring to my glass spine. But the real stickler was that my insurance company tried to cancel their policy on some trivial grounds, resulting in a battle in getting what I was owed. I was now without a car, I had no partner, I was sleeping on the floor of my dad's house, and I was living in, literally, backbreaking pain.

But remember, we're only at the beginning of the workout.

It was time to see what the class instructor had in store for me, and, if my current warm-up was anything to go by, then I'd rather eat shit out of a piss kettle, than see what else this session had in store.

Just as the warm up had felt like the workout, the next part of the class would lay another proverbial smack down. My beloved dog, Honey, died too. I don't care what anyone says, losing a pet isn't that much different to losing a person. There isn't a lot in this world that can show you the unconditional love a dog can, and a time like this, when I felt so low, like everyone had left me, my Honey, who didn't care what cards I was being dealt, had gone too.

And still life had some more shit to throw at me.

My stepfather, someone who I considered as equal to my own dad, had a heart complication and needed an immediate triple heart bypass. I've known a lot of loss in years gone by, and I was staring in the face of losing yet another important role model in my life.

But we have still only just got past the warm up remember? There's more to come, because, a couple of weeks after his operation, he contracted septicaemia from the surgery stitches, and came as close to death as anyone can.

We are now in full session mode. The music is blaring. Get ready for the first exercise – things are about to get even worse.

Just as my stepdad entered recovery, in late 2019, I start getting trolled on fucking social media. I'd started being a PT at a spit-and-sawdust type of gym (the ones where cardio is an afterthought, dumbbells start at 100kg, and grunting is just how you communicate), and I'd now found myself at the forefront of a lot of the member's negativity. This was the type of place that harboured what I like to call the 'elitist brigade'. The types of people, who had probably been bullied in school, so they found a cult like herd mentality in their local gym, where their 'geek' would be revered. Ironically these people, with a chip on their shoulder, found it OK to berate and mock others who didn't fit into their 'live and die by the metal' attitude. Needless to say, they didn't like personal trainers. To them, a personal trainer was a step aerobics instructor who facilitated fluff to old women, which wasn't helped by the owner, who surrounded himself with young impressionable 'lifters', who thought they were God's gift to the iron bar. This is what insecure bullies do. Surround themselves with likeminded impressionable idiots.

Now, when I started to train a well-known girl in this facility, everyone had an opinion, including the owner, who took it upon himself to tell her how bad a trainer he thought I was, for no reason other than jealousy. Luckily, this girl valued me and told me what he said. I'd spent years taking shit off people, I wasn't going to let this happen now, especially feeling the way I did, so a confrontation occurred whereby the owner was made to look like the idiot he was in front of his adoring crowd, resulting in me leaving the gym immediately. I was now without a place to work.

A few days later, and my phone started to alert me that someone was commenting on my Twitter page. Then another, and another, then another. Every two minutes I was receiving messages from people I had never met, who were now trolling me on Twitter calling me every name under the sun, denigrating what I did, who I was and even saying that I was killing some of my clients. It then escalated into intimidation; friends of theirs who were fighters started messaging me inviting me to fight, saying they'd come and visit me to sort it out. It was relentless and went on and on for weeks on end. It almost pushed me over the edge. I grew up fighting as a kid, I had to. With a stepmother who used mental abuse as if it was her favourite a toy and being bullied at school, I surrounded myself with people who took shit from no one. That's why I loved being part of the Three Amigos, a tightknit gang that had your back when others tried to stab at it. Again, I didn't want to tell you this until now, because I didn't want you to think differently about who I was, or change the flavour of the rest of the story. I wanted you to get to know me first as a positive, strong, successful healthy, person.

But, as I have said all along, even the most beautiful, healthy, successful people are wracked with vulnerabilities, insecurities and fear.

And now mine had come to swallow me whole.

Now, my inner circle had gone, the Amigos had gone, and here I was, alone against a whole gym and their dickless fraternity. I wanted revenge more than anything in the world; I wanted to fight; I wanted to go back and get the owner and some of the ringleaders for what they did. But I also knew that this thought process would take me somewhere that I couldn't return from. It was this part of the 'workout', that made me realise I was in a really bad place.

I was slipping into darkness.

The black oil sludge of depression slowed me down like wading through thick quicksand. I was angry, upset, defensive and was immersing myself in every small hiccup that I'd experienced on the way … and magnifying it by a hundred. The trolling was the tip of the iceberg. They'd achieved what they set out to achieve just like all trolls do. I'd inadvertently given them the power and I felt useless that I couldn't get justice. With everything else that had happened, I'd had enough.

I started looking for a way to get out. I didn't want to carry on with this intensity anymore. I wanted to fold my hand and throw my gym towel in. My time in the class was done, but like most group exercise, once you're in, you're in. The workout still had the main proponent and the finisher.

It was time for another blow. What had the shit-magnet in the sky have in store for me now?

The stress had accumulated and presented itself in the form of Bell's Palsy on the left side of my face. Given that I'd spent the most of my twenties trading off of how I looked, this was a hard pill to swallow. Unfortunately, my nervous system had other ideas and I'm still left with some of the effects to this day.

But the madness still wasn't over.

Life needed to dole out another punch, and then another one, and then another one. The never-ending gruelling class still wasn't over. They say that fighters never quit. It's an easy thing to say when you're not fighting. When life is constantly throwing shit at you, and when it feels like no one understands the pain and the heartache that you consistently have to go through, it can get too much. The trudging through the mud of misery to at least try and get onto hard ground tires you out. It's all too easy to say 'cheer up' or 'keep a PMA – Positive Mental Attitude'. People who say those things have often never felt themselves in true hardship, true depression. They generally live simple lives, never putting themselves in harm's way. I had laid everything out on the line, more than once. Sure, I consider myself privileged. I didn't grow up on a council estate, I didn't have to endure bad teachers and poor parents. But the mind doesn't work like that. Poor mental health can affect the richest, most successful people in the world. How you deal with it is down to you. Merely thinking positively does NOT get you out of depression, just like eating more doesn't bring you out of anorexia nervosa, or just 'getting on the treadmill' doesn't end obesity. These flagrant flippant comments are from the ignorant, who have no understanding of anything other than their own lives.

Time for the class finisher, the last part of the workout where we see who can take the pain and who can't.

The penultimate instalment of pain came from my arch nemesis, the stepmother who had caused me so much anxiety and heartache in my teenage years. If ever there was a stereotype that rang true in my life, it is the evil stepmother who moved in with my father when I was 11. After manipulating her way in, I was forcibly ostracised from my father as a kid and was subjected to years of mental abuse, chipping itself away at my confidence and self-esteem. It is only now, almost twenty years later, that the police recognise some of the tactics used by controlling partners/parents. For me, it's twenty years too late.

However, there was some justice to be had, or so I thought, as she had filed for divorce from my father in my year of fresh hell, 2019. She had got bored with berating me and my family and discarded my father when she felt he no longer offered her anything (about six months after he had retired and no money was coming in).

Great, I thought, finally, now our family can move on. Dad can build the bridges with the rest of his family that she put so much energy into breaking. But this was only the start. It was now carte blanche for her to show her true colours. It's important to note here that she had two children with my father – my two half-brothers who I treat as my own children and are the actual subject of the 'finisher' in this class of Satan's arsehole.

Not content with creating as much chaos as she possibly could during the divorce, she wanted to be able to control my two brothers and had applied to the courts to get full custody. Much like her personality trait of causing as much harm as possible, she wasn't content with having them just live with her. No, she wanted to be able to legally stop them from having any correspondence with my father and me. She had been incredibly jealous of my father's relationship with me growing up, and she had set out to destroy any relationship her own sons could have with us for her own selfish gain.

I was now facing another court case just to fight to see my own brothers.

Mental.

Let's quickly recap for those at the back:

I'd lost Trish, my favourite client to cancer.
I'd herniated a fourth disc in my back.

I'd split up with the love of my life.

I was sleeping on the floor of my dad's house.

I was now in a legal case.

I'd written my car off.

My stepfather had nearly died.

My beloved dog *had* died.

I'd been publicly bullied on social media.

I now looked like Two Face from *Batman*.

And my evil stepmother took me court to see my own family.

I think's that all of it?

Oh no, one more. I forgot the part of the class where the trainer says there is 'one more for luck', and makes you complete one last lunge; a purge.

Prior to the 'fuckening' of 2019, I had been working hard on the private gym project that would change the way I worked in the future. Something to pull me out of the oil slick. Something to give me hope. I had been working on the project for about 18 months and it looked like it was coming to fruition. At last, there was a light at the end of the tunnel. A shining light amongst the darkness that surrounded me, A studio of my own again, after all the years of having to put up with shake weights, placentas and Ab toners. A home I could call my own, a place that could offer me some stability. A place that I had spent hours and hours on planning permissions, architectural drawings, structural engineers and equipment providers trying to sell me expensive equipment on piss poor leases.

All of it was gone in a second when the landlord decided to pull out of the deal, cowering behind the managing agents who now had to give me the bad news.

With this, mentally and physically, I was finished. All hope gone. Emotionally, I was shot.

And then I did something I'm not proud of. I started looking for someone who could sell me a gun.

I had had enough. This was it, the end. I felt like killing

myself was the easiest way out. Nothing mattered anymore. No one mattered anymore. Life was no longer worth it. My business could be sold and my assets could be left to my brothers so they were financially stable in life.

I wrote my last will and testament.

And then I wrote this chapter, just so everyone would know the truth —'the final chapter of a life less ordinary, but no less awful.

But then something happened, after I wrote all this down.

I felt better. A little.

Whatever my past had written for me, I'm lucky to have defiance, stubbornness and resolve in my blood. I started to see a small thread of hope. For all of my adult life, I had expressed myself through my brawn, but after expressing myself emotionally, demons for the first time were exorcised.

A few days after finishing the book, I sought out a psychiatrist who, whether it was pure coincidence or a subconscious attempt at entering further into my own self-defeating hellhole, aptly had the surname 'Slaughter'. I didn't know whether to laugh or to cry BUT … as they say, you can't have slaughter without laughter.

The following weeks were a conflict between the idea of shrinking my own head with a .45 or seeing past this stage of my life and fixing it with a doctor. I'd never really liked the idea of 'seeking help' for an issue of the mind. I'd always grown up dealing with things on my own and in my own way – and when I looked in the mirror all I saw was a healthy person, but, of course, my issues hid under the skin, deep. I could finally see that being fit on the outside did not mean I was fit on the inside. Weird, given that my own profession was people seeking help from me, I assumed, arrogantly, that I had every tool to cope with my own breakdown, but I clearly hadn't. I'd found myself wallowing in the thick oil sludge for too long. There were things that were out of my control and some things that weren't. The things I could control needed looking at.

It was time to focus on my mind, instead of keeping company with misery. It was time I fixed myself. I'd forgotten what kept me alive. I had forgotten what it was to enjoy something, what it was like to look forward to something that was mine, something I had complete control of. It was time to make some serious changes, and it was probably time to say goodbye to the fitness industry.

And with that revelation, my mind-set changed and things around me started to *feel* better. I realised, as should you, that people always come and go. Relationships form and relationships break. Pets die and people get ill. It doesn't make it any easier, but it is a fact of life that doesn't mean ending your own.

Not long after this revelation, I moved from my dad's floor to a penthouse in the leafy countryside of Hertfordshire, using the remainder of my savings. I found myself a new place to work doing what I'm doing now. I eventually found someone who could genuinely help with my back issues. I allowed myself to meet someone who became the rock in my life and I learned that I still had love in me and could be loved again. I had finally got a grip of what life now meant to me. I still had – still do – have dark days; that thick sludge is always lurking in the background, but the more I respected myself, the more it stayed behind me.

The curse lifted just a little to see a ray of light.

Opportunities presented themselves to me, just like they did before, but now I had grown to understand them better and appreciate them more.

I was me again. Me 2.0.

REBOOT

As the world descended into the first lockdown of 2020, and with the end already written, I sat down to write the beginning stories to this book, my origin. I wanted this book to be part ode to the industry that gave me everything, good and bad, and part warning of the perils and pearls of wisdom I received as a PT. I will always have my heart in the fitness game, no matter how far removed from it I am.

I hope you have all enjoyed this book as much as I have writing it. It helped me.

If you're a PT out there, I hope you can resonate with some of the things I have said. There are so many more aspects of health and fitness to be excited about, as long as you have the energy for it. Be wary of the 'quick buck' kids, know your target audience, be professional, stay off your iPhones during sessions and respect the clients you have. Hell, we may have even trained the same people at some point! Get in touch and share your story with me. I can be found on my beloved social media. Oh, the irony.

For those of you who have a PT or are looking to hire a PT yourself, understand it is not always rosy on our side of the garden wall. Don't bargain your trainer's rates down. If you like them and think they are good, then pay them what they are worth. Be confident that your trainer has access to new knowledge because we ARE getting there gradually. Better, more advanced research is paving the future for fitness and wellness as a whole. I am hopeful that we are moving in the right direction, and finally people are starting to realise the bullshit from the good shit.

And this is where I pay my dues to a career that has been so fulfilling, so demoralising but has also given me some of the most belly aching laughs and heart-breaking goodbyes I'll ever have. If you're an average schmo about to undertake your qualification, or are deciding on a career change into the fitness industry, you have so much to look forward to.

And just as I finished the first draft of this book, that's taken me nearly eighteen months to condense most of my life to write, I go and receive email that was truly unexpected:

Dear Matt,

I trust this finds you well. I must apologise that it has taken us so long to get everything in order but we wanted to be the first to tell you that the landlord has changed his mind and finally given the go ahead, and we anticipate that the gym would potentially be ready for opening this November – if of course you're still willing?

Please let us know and we will send you out the contract later today. In the meantime could you ping us over the scheduled equipment list and we'll pass this on to the landlord.

Please let us know when you can jump on a conference call to discuss.

And just like that, the fitness industry wants me back.

So, is this the end … or the beginning again?

You do you remember that I said that I never turn anything down, right?

A SPECIAL THANKS TO...

Those that stuck by me, supported me all the way through a turbulent near twenty years of using disinfectant hand wash after every client session, The Mogs, Ms. Roach – the best lawyer on planet earth, Rich Denham (my formatter), Nath, Eli, Heather the mothership, Big Daddy Phil, Jono, my second family – The Burns, The Three Amigos, The editor massive – The Trows, The Coveys, The Kayes, The Haraldssons, D.Z, all the real people behind all the characters in this book, The Portanias, Dean at Contours FX, the equipment providers (you know who you are), Frank Boi Smith, Ali & Renata, Si Stratton, Rob Riches for getting me started, Phil Learney for initially showing me the way, David Sutton and Andy McKenzie for listening to a wet behind the ears PT, Chris Sritharan, David McGettigan, Bergman Interiors for outstanding gym design, Gina B, Rosie Millen, all the guys at The Armitage, all the guys at Igloo, the crew at Inanch, Gaynor for being my longest serving client, and bicep curls, brown rice and boiled chicken. Not forgetting the most interesting, annoying, funny, loveable, horrible clients and fellow PTs I've had throughout my career.

There are so many other stories and incidents I wanted to share but they will have to wait for another day. Without you guys I wouldn't have any of them!'

And, last but not least, the fitness industry.

A SPECIAL FUCK YOU TO ...

Normally, like any other book, this would be the bit where you reflect on that hollow void you get when you've finished the best book you've ever read (joke). But first I must acknowledge those who I want to say a massive fuck you to. Not because I'm bitter (well only slightly) but because it took me over 2,000 hours to write 78,000 words so I think I'm entitled to a little revenge. Anyway, without the 'fuck yous' I wouldn't have had the motivation to write this book, so I guess in a weird way I should be thanking you...

Anyway, a massive fuck you goes to ...

Mr Burpee, for inventing the most unpleasant exercise in history. You sir, take pole position – clients hate them and so should PTs.

More fuck yous go to: *Love Island*, Ab toners, cabbage soup, MR, the pillock who owns PC (and I don't mean political correctness; as you are now probably aware I broke that whole idea very early on), 'fitness' influencers, sleep deprivation, fat freezing, those that still owe me money, the assault bike and sled pushes (anyone can attest to this), skinny water, 4.30am starts and

10pm finishes, fitniz trolls – you know who you are and I haven't forgotten you, fat loss lollipops, Kim Kardashian's arse (it has a lot to answer for) and slipped discs.

Oh, and of course how could I forget, the biggest one of them all...

The fitness industry.

Printed in Great Britain
by Amazon

47120888R00152